# Layout
## for
# Duct
# Fittings

By

LEO A. MEYER

INDOOR ENVIRONMENT
TECHNICIAN'S LIBRARY

LAMA BOOKS
HVAC BOOKS
THAT WORK

# FOREWORD

Computerized layout machines are so efficient that sheet metal pattern drafting is becoming a lost art. Yet here at LAMA Books we frequently receive requests for material on how to lay out certain fittings—mostly duct fittings. We feel that there is a need for layout knowledge for the many small shops that do not have layout machines. Layout knowledge is also valuable for those who want a fuller knowledge of the trade. This book is designed to meet those needs.

## Indoor Environment Technician's Library

This book is part of the *Indoor Environment Technician's Library*. These are practical books that you can use for training or as reference. These books apply to all areas of the indoor environment industry, such as:

Heating, ventilating, and air conditioning
Energy management
Indoor air quality
Commercial and industrial sheet metal work
Residential sheet metal work
Building commissioning
Testing, adjusting, and balancing

If you are a supervisor training others, you will find that the *Indoor Environment Technician's Library* can make your training sessions easier.

Leo A. Meyer

LAMA Books
2381 Sleepy Hollow Avenue
Hayward CA 94545-3429
888-452-6244
FAX: 510-785-1099
www.lama@lamabooks.com

ISBN 0-88069-028-3, ISBN 9780-88069-028-7
3rd printing 2010

# TABLE OF CONTENTS

# 1

# *LAYING OUT PATTERNS*

Since you have decided to read this book on laying out duct fittings, we assume that you understand duct fabrication and are familiar with the basic layout tools (Fig. 1). You probably know how to lay out straight duct. This book explains how to lay out fittings—the items that are not straight duct.

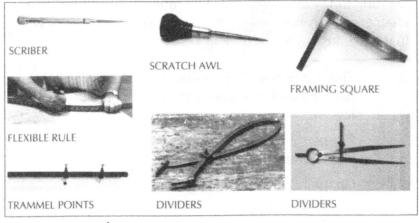

SCRIBER

SCRATCH AWL

FRAMING SQUARE

FLEXIBLE RULE

TRAMMEL POINTS

DIVIDERS

DIVIDERS

*Fig. 1: Layout tools*

## TERMS

You should know the following terms used in layout work. Terms for sheet metal work often vary in different areas, but the following terms are generally used.

**Fittings**—Sheet metal duct items such as elbows, offsets, and transitions that are not straight duct.

**Layout**—The process of drawing patterns for sheet metal objects.

**To lay out**—To draw the patterns for a sheet metal object.

**Stretchout**—The length of a pattern, not counting the seams or edge allowances.

**Pattern**—A sheet metal item drawn flat. The final pattern has all the allowances for seams and edges added.

# BASICS OF LAYOUT

If you understand the basics of layout, you will find that learning to lay out particular duct fittings is easy. The first chapters of this book cover the basics you need to know that make layout much easier:

- ❑ The rest of this chapter covers methods of marking patterns on metal and some practical math for layout.
- ❑ Chapter 2 covers connectors that you need to allow for on your patterns.
- ❑ Chapter 3 covers the all-important idea of true lengths.

## Choose Your Method

For every pattern you lay out, there are different ways of doing it. To simplify, let's call them:

- ❑ Very accurate
- ❑ Standard practice
- ❑ Shortcut

In general, all three are the same method, but some versions cut down on points and lines, and they sidestep formal geometric constructions. In general, the shorter the method, the less accurate the pattern. But there's a place for all three ways. It just depends on the situation.

You would choose the **very accurate** method if you were making a welded, heavy gage stainless steel elbow. The extra time spent in layout would be gained back by faster and easier fabrication.

Usually the **standard practice** method is used. Over the years, sheet metal workers have developed these ways that can get the pattern done in an acceptable time with all the accuracy needed.

The **shortcut** method is usually the standard practice method with the points and lines of the pattern cut to a minimum. It is used when time is scarce and the fitting will be hidden in an attic or covered by insulation.

You need to use judgment when you choose how to lay out a pattern. Time and appearance of the fitting are key factors. But duct leakage is another very important consideration. In these days of high energy costs, the leakage of heated or cooled air from the duct is costly. This means fittings and duct must be fit together well. Commercial jobs often specify the percentage of leakage that will be allowed.

## Check Your Pattern

Four principles of layout can help you check your pattern quickly.

First of all, as you lay out different types of fittings, study the general shape of each pattern. A particular type of fitting always has the same general shape. A square-to-round has a particular shape and an offset square-to-round has a similar but slightly different shape. The same is true for a round tee pattern or a round elbow pattern. If you have a general idea what the pattern will look like, you may be able to see quickly if the layout is in error.

A second check on your patterns is that the curves on a pattern are almost always smooth. If the points you develop for a curve show an abrupt change of direction, you should recheck your layout.

A third check is knowing that certain lines on patterns always form square corners. As this book describes different layouts, the square corners will be pointed out. If these corners on your patterns are not 90°, your layout is probably not correct.

A fourth method is to check mating parts. For example, a rectangular transition is typically four pieces. The mating seams must be the same length.

# LAYOUT ON METAL

Almost all duct patterns are drawn directly on metal. This requires some different methods than when using a pencil and paper. You will develop your own methods, but for starters, remember the following:

- ❏ Have all of your layout tools handy.

- ❏ Start at the lower left corner of the sheet. Hold a square to the corner to check it for 90°. Most sheets are square, but it's always a good idea to check.

- ❏ Use the framing square to square up the first pattern line from the bottom of the sheet (Fig. 2). You will use this line to measure from, so if it is square, all the rest of the lines will be square.

- ❏ Use this squared line and the bottom of the sheet as measuring bases. Figure 2 shows how parallel lines 12" apart would be marked and drawn. Squaring up

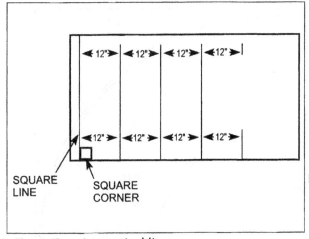

SQUARE
LINE

SQUARE
CORNER

*Fig. 2: Drawing vertical lines*

each line takes too much time, so 12" is measured at the bottom and top of the squared line. Then the line is drawn to these marks.

❑ Draw all the vertical lines first and then all the horizontal lines. (Of course, if it makes you happy, you can draw the horizontal lines first.) The point is to draw all the lines in one direction and then those in the other direction to be sure you don't forget some lines.

❑ To save time, don't draw unneeded lines. Usually you need to mark only bend lines and cutting lines. As you gain experience, you will learn to get along with fewer and fewer lines.

❑ Use up the scrap. You will soon learn to rapidly calculate the size of metal you will need for a pattern. Always check the scrap rack to check for a suitable piece. It gets rid of scrap and therefore saves money.

## Marking

Patterns should be marked to show the number of pieces needed and to give bending instructions. Often someone else in the shop will form and assemble the fittings. Even if you do it yourself, it may be several days before you form the pieces. Markings remind you quickly what the piece is for and ensure that you do not bend something "wrong side out." Here are some of the principles of marking:

❑ Marking methods vary from shop to shop. Follow the method preferred by the shop you are working in.

❑ Put all marks on the side that will be inside the finished fitting. Everyone assumes that marks are on the inside and will form the piece accordingly. Inside markings leave the outside of the installed duct looking clean and neat.

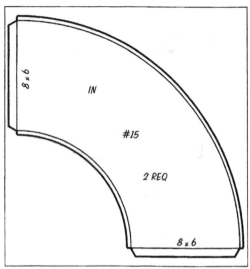

Fig. 3: Markings on an elbow cheek

❑ To be sure there are no mistakes, mark each pattern "IN" to indicate the inside.

❑ Mark the size of the finished duct on each end of the pattern. The first number is always the dimension of the pattern. For example, in Fig. 3, the cheek pattern is 8" and the other side of the duct is 6".

❑ Show the number of pieces that are needed. For example, the elbow cheek pattern in Fig. 3 is marked "2 REQ" (2 required). This means that a total of 2 pieces are needed. When marking the second cheek, take care that IN is marked on the correct side.

❑ Identification numbers on a pattern match the identification numbers on a drawing or sketch. For example, in Fig. 3, the number 15 shows that it is a pattern for the piece numbered 15 on a drawing of the duct run. All of the patterns for one fitting have the same number. For example, a rectangular duct elbow is made up of four pieces, and each of the pieces has the same ID number (Fig. 4). Since a number of different pattern pieces are formed up at

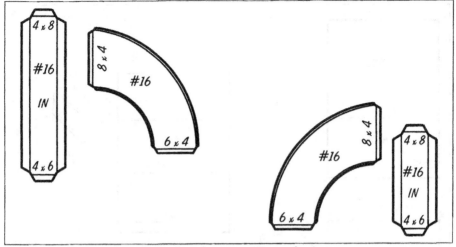

*Fig. 4: Each piece for a fitting has the same ID number*

the same time, the ID numbers make it easy to sort out the pieces when assembling the fittings.

❑ It is usually assumed that the person fabricating the duct knows what allowances and notching are needed for common seams, locks, and edges (such as S & drives, Pittsburgh seams, and TDCs), so instructions for these are not marked on a pattern.

❑ Bends are marked for direction and angle. There are different methods and all are acceptable as long as they are clear. Figure 5 shows various ways of marking bends.

## Copying Patterns

Often you will need several copies of the same pattern. It's good practice to use your original pattern to mark all the rest of the patterns. That way there is less chance of variation. To copy a pattern:

❑ Lay it on the metal so that there will be the least amount of unusable scrap left.

❑ Put a weight on the pattern to hold it in place.

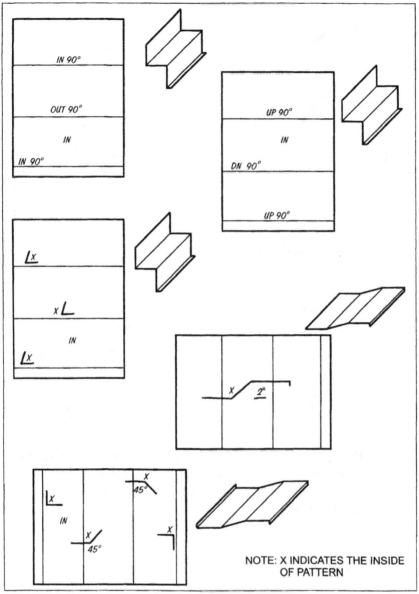

Fig. 5: Different ways to mark bend lines

- ❏ Trace around the edges with a scratch awl.
- ❏ Prick mark through the pattern to mark all bend lines on the copy.

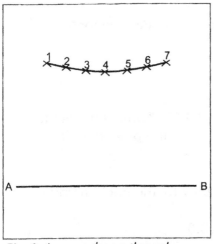

Fig. 6: A curve drawn through points

# Drawing Curves

The curves of some patterns, such as an elbow pattern (Fig. 3), are arcs swung from a center point. But some patterns establish a curve by locating a series of points (Fig. 6). Then a curve has to be drawn through the points. One method of drawing the curve is to bend a flexible steel rule so that it touches each point. Then someone can draw the curve along the bend of the rule. I think that a better way is to learn to draw the curves in freehand. With a little practice you will learn to draw in a smooth curve touching each point. One tip—keep our eye on the point you are drawing **to**, not on where you have been.

# PRACTICAL MATH

You will often use a calculator to figure a length (such as the circumference of a circle). The problem is that the calculator gives the answer in decimals of an inch, and your rule is in fractions. The usual way of converting decimals to fractions is useless. What would you do if you got an answer of $\frac{8}{45}$" when your rule measures in 16ths of an inch?

We call fractions on a rule ($\frac{1}{4}$, $\frac{1}{8}$, $\frac{1}{16}$) **usable fractions**. They are the only fractions that are practical to use for measuring. It is easy to change a decimal to the nearest usable fraction you want to use:

❑ Multiply the **decimal only** by the fraction you want.

❑ Round off the answer to the nearest whole number.

- ❑ Use this as the number above the line for the nearest fraction.

## Example:

You have a calculated length of 4.675" and you want to convert it to the nearest $\frac{1}{16}$". Follow the procedure just described:

- ❑ Multiply the **decimal only** by the fraction you want:

$$0.675 \times 16 = 10.8$$

- ❑ Round off the answer to the nearest whole number:

$$10.8 \text{ rounded off} = 11$$

- ❑ Use this as the top number of the fraction:

$$\frac{11}{16}$$

Therefore, 4.675" to the nearest 16th is $4\frac{11}{16}$".

## Learn Fraction/Decimal Equivalents

Another thing that helps is that gradually you will learn many of the fraction/decimal equivalents. For example, you probably already know that $0.5 = \frac{1}{2}$ and that $0.25 = \frac{1}{4}$. Therefore, if you have a length of 5.259" you know that the equivalent is $5\frac{1}{4}$". The fraction-decimal equivalents you should know are given in Fig. 7.

| EQUIVALENTS | | |
|---|---|---|
| Fraction | | Decimal |
| $\frac{1}{16}$ | = | .0625 |
| $\frac{1}{8}$ | = | .125 |
| $\frac{3}{16}$ | = | .1875 |
| $\frac{1}{4}$ | = | .25 |
| $\frac{5}{16}$ | = | .3125 |
| $\frac{3}{8}$ | = | .375 |
| $\frac{7}{16}$ | = | .4375 |
| $\frac{1}{2}$ | = | .5 |
| $\frac{9}{16}$ | = | .5625 |
| $\frac{5}{8}$ | = | .625 |
| $\frac{11}{16}$ | = | .6875 |
| $\frac{3}{4}$ | = | .75 |
| $\frac{13}{16}$ | = | .8125 |
| $\frac{7}{8}$ | = | .875 |
| $\frac{15}{16}$ | = | .9375 |

Fig. 7: Learn these equivalents to change a fraction to a decimal or a decimal to a fraction

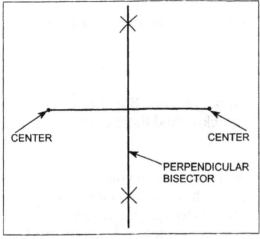

Fig. 8: Perpendicular bisector

# Square Up a Center Point Line

For some layout you need to square up a line at the center point of a given line. This line is called a **perpendicular bisector.** To square up a line at the center point (Fig. 8):

❑ Set the dividers to more than half the length of the given line. The wider the divider setting, the more accurate your construction will be.

❑ Swing arcs above and below the given line, using the two ends of the line as center points.

❑ Draw a line through the intersections of these arcs. This perpendicular bisector cuts the given line in half.

# Divide a Line into Equal Parts

In some layouts (such as round elbows and round tees) you have to divide a line (the stretchout of the pattern) into equal parts. Standard practice for many layouts is to divide the stretchout into 12 equal spaces. Use dividers to obtain the equal spaces:

❑ Estimate the setting for the dividers.

❑ Step off the spaces.

- ❏ The first try will be off. Adjust the dividers and step off again.
- ❏ Repeat until you step off 12 equal spaces.

This sounds like a long drawn-out process. But after you do it for a while it can be done quickly. And there are tricks to make it faster.

One is to divide the stretchout in half. Then you have cut your job in half because you only have to step off 6 spaces. One way to divide the stretchout is to use your dividers to locate the halfway point as shown in Fig. 8. A faster method is to divide the measurement in half in your head. For example, the stretchout for a 6" diameter pipe is $18\frac{7}{8}$":

- ❏ Half of 18 is 9.
- ❏ Half of $\frac{7}{8}$ is $\frac{7}{16}$. (To cut a fraction in half, just double the bottom number.)
- ❏ Therefore, half of $18\frac{7}{8}$" is $9\frac{7}{16}$".

You can even divide the $9\frac{7}{16}$" in half to get the quarter point on the stretchout. Then you only have to step off 3 spaces to get the dividers set to the right spacing:

- ❏ Half of 9 is $4\frac{1}{2}$.
- ❏ Half of $\frac{7}{16}$ is $\frac{7}{32}$.
- ❏ Don't bother to add $4\frac{1}{2} + \frac{7}{32}$. Just measure $4\frac{1}{2}$" on the line and then measure another $\frac{7}{32}$". That's the quarter point of an $18\frac{7}{8}$" stretchout.

Once the dividers are set to the right division, you can step off 12 equal spaces on the line. Step off 6 spaces to the halfway point. You might have to adjust the dividers a little because of human error. Then step off the other half of the stretchout.

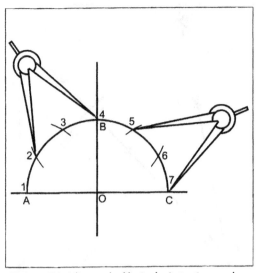

Fig. 9: Dividing a half-circle into 6 equal spaces

# Divide a Half Circle into Equal Spaces

Just as a line is divided into 12 equal spaces, circles are often divided into 12 spaces. To save time, use a half-circle divided into 6 spaces. This is even easier than dividing a line. Draw the half-circle (Fig. 9) and do the following:

❏ Square up a line from the center point O. This gives 2 quarter-circles.

❏ With the dividers set at the radius of the circle, use point B as a center point and swing arcs to mark points 2 and 6.

❏ Next use points A and C as center points and mark points 3 and 5.

That's it! The half-circle is divided into 6 spaces. The points are always numbered from 1 to 7 as shown in Figure 9.

# Draw an Arc through 3 Points

When laying out cheek patterns for slanted cheek elbows, you establish three points for the heel or throat curve. Then you need to swing an arc that will pass through the three points. Figure 10 shows how to find the center point for the arc that passes through 3 given points:

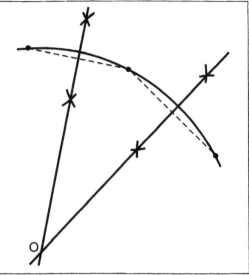

Fig. 10: Swing an arc through three points

- ☐ Connect the points with two lines.

- ☐ Erect perpendicular bisectors to each line.

- ☐ The intersection of these two bisectors is the center point O for the arc.

## LET'S MOVE ON

Now you have the basics of marking patterns on metal. The next chapter covers the practices for making allowances for duct connections and seams.

# 2  *MAKING CONNECTIONS*

## DUCT CONNECTIONS AND SEAMS

**Duct connections** are used to join two pieces of duct.
**Seams** are used to close the long edge of a piece of duct.
Connections and seams are an important part of duct layout
because they require that some allowance must be added to
the pattern. The type of connection also determines the way
in which the corners of a pattern are notched.

## TRANSVERSE DUCT CONNECTIONS

Two pieces of rectangular duct are connected by means of
transverse duct connections. Don't confuse this term with a
similar one:

- ❏ **Transverse duct connection** is a general term that
  means any method of connecting two pieces of
  rectangular duct.

- ❏ **Transverse duct connector** (commonly called TDC)
  means a type of patented duct connector made by
  several manufacturers.

Most rectangular duct is connected by either S & drive or
TDC connectors. S & drives are used in residential work and
sometimes for smaller duct in commercial work. TDC is
used for commercial work and sometimes for large
residential jobs.

# S & Drives

**S & drives** (**S & D**) consist of two different **cleats**:

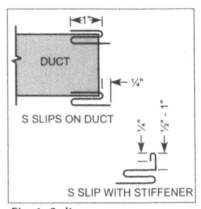

*Fig. 1: S slips*

- ❑ The **S slip** (Fig. 1) generally slides onto a straight edge of the wide side of the duct. It keeps the two pieces of duct from collapsing into each other. For wider duct (about 18" or more), the S slip is made with a stiffener (Fig. 1) to keep the side of the duct from sagging.

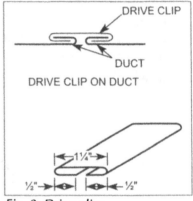

*Fig. 2: Drive clips*

- ❑ The **drive clip** (Fig. 2) slides on hooked edges that are formed on the duct. (It is called a drive clip because it is driven on with a hammer.) The drive clip keeps the two pieces of duct from pulling apart. Drives are generally used on the small side of the duct to cut down on the length they need to be driven.

To make up a joint with S & drives, the S slips are put on the end of one duct. Then the second duct is slid into place. The drive clips are slid onto the hooked edges. The drive is left 1" longer than the duct side so that ½" extends beyond the duct at each end of the clip. These ½" edges are hammered around the corner of the duct so that the drive cannot slip off. More important, it closes the corner of the connection to cut down air leakage.

S & drives work better on the smaller sizes of duct. For duct larger than 18" wide, they are difficult to drive on.

S & drive connections allow more air leakage than TDC connections. Job specifications often require that S & drive connections be sealed against leakage by applying some type of sealant.

# TDC (Transverse Duct Connectors)

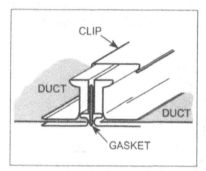

*Fig. 3: Typical slip-on TDC*

**TDC**s are manufactured connectors that come in various designs, depending on the company that furnishes them. Some types slip over the straight edge of the duct (Fig. 3). Another type is formed in the shop on the end of the duct (Fig. 4) by a special rollforming machine. All types have a gasket between the flanges (Fig. 3) and a method of filling in the corners (Fig. 4). The corners are connected by means of a bolt or a clip.

These connectors save time, and if they are installed properly, air leakage is kept to a minimum.

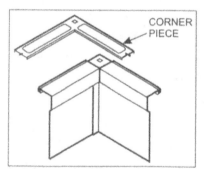

*Fig. 4: The TDC edge can be formed on the end of the duct by a rollforming machine*

## Tap-in Lock

When a small rectangular duct is tapped into the side of a larger duct (Fig. 5), a **tap-in** is used. The part of the **tap-in lock** that goes into the large duct is cut to form ¾" wide tabs (Fig. 6). This small size makes the tabs easier to tap over since you have to reach inside the tap-in to hammer the tabs over. To make it easier to reach into the tap-in, it is seldom over 6" long.

The tap-in in Fig. 5 is 90° to the large duct (square to the duct). However, many tap-ins are **sweep taps** (Fig. 6) with about a 6" throat radius. A sweep tap creates less turbulence in the airstream.

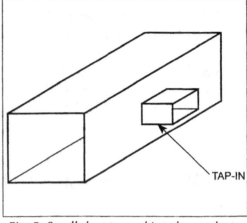

Fig. 5: Small duct tapped into larger duct

## ROUND DUCT CONNECTORS

The traditional joint for round duct is the **beaded and crimped joint** (Fig. 7). However, the **draw band** (Fig. 7) and the **beaded coupling** (Fig. 7) are also used.

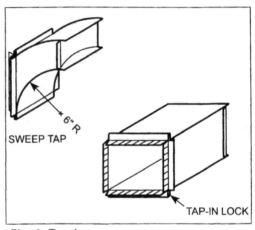

Fig. 6: Tap-ins

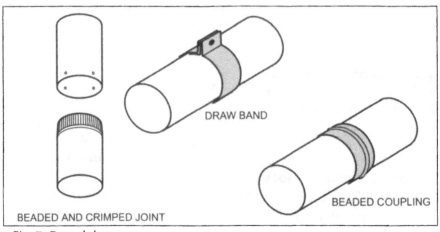

Fig. 7: Round duct connectors

Special manufactured draw bands are used for round spiral duct.

## THE PITTSBURGH SEAM

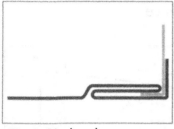

*Fig. 8: Pittsburgh seam*

For the lengthwise seams of long corners of straight duct and fittings, the **Pittsburgh seam** (Fig. 8) is almost always used. An allowance is turned to 90° on one long side of the duct, and the Pittsburgh is formed on the other long edge. The 90° bend is inserted into the Pittsburgh lock, and the edge on the lock is bent over (Fig. 8).

The allowance for the edge that fits into the Pittsburgh is $\frac{1}{4}$" for straight duct and $\frac{3}{16}$" for the curves on fittings. The Pittsburgh is formed on a rollforming machine. The allowance for the Pittsburgh is usually 1", but this will vary slightly (from 1" up to $1\frac{1}{2}$") depending on the rollforming machine that is used. When you work in a new shop, always check to find out the allowance that is used.

## ALLOWANCES

Most of the patterns in this book are drawn without allowances for seams and edges because the book concentrates on the basic pattern layout. However, for an actual pattern, allowances must be added. Allowances and notching vary from shop to shop and area to area.

These are Pittsburgh seam allowances:

- ❏ Pittsburgh—Add 1" (can vary from 1" to $1\frac{1}{2}$")
- ❏ Edge to fit into Pittsburgh seam—Add $\frac{1}{4}$" on straight duct and $\frac{3}{16}$" on curved edges

These are common connection allowances:

- ❑ S & drives—Add $\frac{1}{2}$"

- ❑ Rollformed TDC—Add according to machine and manufacturer

- ❑ Slip-on TDC—No added allowance

If slip-on TDCs are to be used to connect pieces with slanted or curved sides (such as elbows and offsets), there must be a straight section for the TDC to fit on. This means that part of the basic pattern must be straight, not curved or slanted (Fig. 9). Most TDCs require $1\frac{1}{2}$" of straight on the basic pattern. However, when you are using a new type of TDC, always check for the amount of straight that it requires.

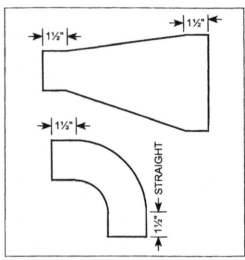

Fig. 9: Slip-on TDCs require a straight portion on curved or slanted fittings

Figure 10 shows elbow patterns for a slip-on TDC. The **finished length** of the elbow is to the edge of the metal at the duct connection. Note the 8" and $6\frac{1}{2}$" dimensions. The drawing for this elbow called for an 8" throat. Since $1\frac{1}{2}$" has to be straight at each end, the actual **throat radius** must be $6\frac{1}{2}$". This is important because, in many cases, the overall length of the duct run is critical.

The Pittsburgh allowance is notched back $1\frac{1}{2}$" on the cheek, throat, and heel patterns (Fig. 10) so that it does not interfere with putting on the TDC.

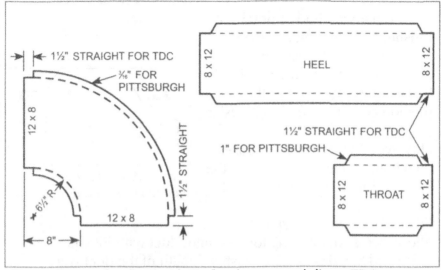

Fig. 10: Patterns for elbow with Pittsburgh seams and slip-on TDC connections

# NOTCHING

Different connections require different types of notching. Notching methods vary from shop to shop. Figures 11 through 17 show common methods of notching.

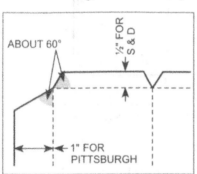

Fig. 11: Notching for Pittsburgh and S and drives

Figure 11 shows a typical notching method for a **Pittsburgh seam and S & drives**. The notches are at about a 60° angle. The angle on the seam gets the edge of the Pittsburgh out of the way of the S & drives. The angle on the S & drive allowance makes it easier to start the drive clip and the S slip.

The bottom of the notch goes to the bend line for the drive. The bend lines are shown here with dashed lines, but in actual practice these lines are seldom drawn.

An alternate method of notching a **Pittsburgh seam and S & drives** is shown in Fig. 12. These notches are cut deeper than the bend lines. Some shops prefer this method because it makes it easier to get the S & drives on. However, this method increases the chance of air leakage, and the finished joints should be sealed.

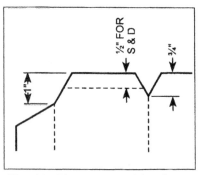

*Fig. 12: Alternate notching for Pittsburgh and S & drives*

Figure 13 shows the typical allowance and notching for a straight duct with Pittsburgh seam and S & drives. The finished length of the duct is to the bend for the drive. Allowances for S & drives on both end of a duct take up a total of 1". Therefore, if the length of duct is made from a 36" wide sheet, the finished length will be 35".

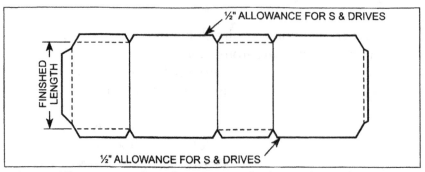

*Fig. 13: Allowances and notching for straight duct with S & drives*

Figure 14 shows typical allowances and notches for a **duct elbow with S & drives**. Note that the curved edge to fit into the Pittsburgh is $\frac{3}{16}$". It is smaller than the normal $\frac{1}{4}$" used on straight duct because the metal must be stretched or shrunk when a 90° bend is made on a curve. The finished length of the fitting is to the bend for the drive.

Figure 15 shows notching for **straight duct with Pittsburgh seam and slip-on TDC.** The seam allowance for the

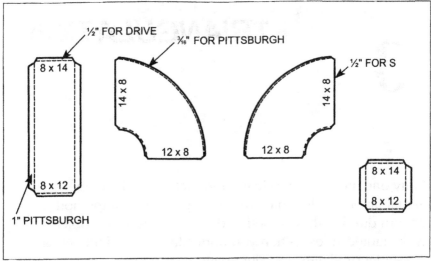

*Fig. 14: Allowances and notching for elbow with Pittsburgh and S & drives*

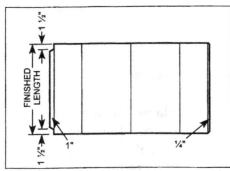

*Fig. 15: Notching for straight duct with Pittsburgh seam and TDC*

Pittsburgh is notched back 1½" so that the TDC can be slipped on.

Figure 16 shows the straight and seam allowance for an **offset with slip-on TDC**. The drawing for the duct run specified a length of 21" for the offset. Because of the 1½" straight on each end, the S part of the offset is 18".

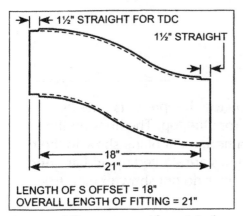

*Fig. 16: Offset pattern with straight for TDC*

# 3  *TRIANGULATION*

Only one more thing to learn and then we will get to the actual layout of duct patterns. Triangulation is a method of pattern drafting that is used to develop patterns for objects with slanted sides. When you understand the principles of triangulation, laying out duct patterns is easy.

There are only two simple ideas to learn about triangulation:

- ❑ True lengths
- ❑ Triangulating from two known points

First, you should understand the term **plane**. The term simply means a **flat surface**. An example of a horizontal plane is a tabletop. An example of a vertical plane is a wall. An example of a slanted plane is a loading ramp.

# TRUE LENGTHS

A **plan view** is a view from the top. It represents lines as they are seen looking down from the top. The lines on the plan view that are really on a horizontal plane show in their true length. However, some lines are slanted up and are **not** on a horizontal plane. These lines do not show in their true length.

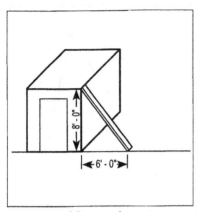

*Fig. 1: Building and 2 x 4*

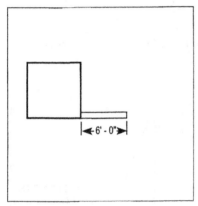

*Fig. 2: Plan view of the building in Fig. 1*

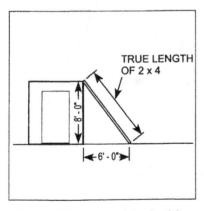

*Fig. 3: Side views of the building in Fig. 2*

Look at Fig. 1. It is a building with a 2 × 4 piece of lumber leaning against it. The building is 8 feet high and the 2 × 4 is 10 feet long. The bottom of the 2 × 4 is 6 feet away from the building.

A plan view (Fig. 2) shows the length of the 2 × 4 as 6 feet because a plan view can only show horizontal distances. However, if we know that the building is 8 feet high, we can determine how long the 2 × 4 is from the length shown on the plan view. It could be done mathematically, but in layout we do it by simply drawing a side view. From the side view of the building in Fig. 3, the 2 × 4 could be measured (if it were drawn to scale).

Now consider the sheet metal pyramid in Fig. 4. This is not a duct fitting, but it is a simple way to see the principles of true lengths. The pyramid is $2\frac{1}{4}$" high. To lay out the pattern for one side of the pyramid, you need to know the length of the corner lines. Since this is a centered pyramid (the center of the pyramid is in the center of the square), all the corner lines (lines AO, BO, CO, and DO) are the same length.

On the plan view (Fig. 4), the bottom lines of the pyramid (lines AB, BC, CD, and DA) lie on the horizontal plane, so these show as true lengths. On the other hand, the corner lines (such as AO) slant from the bottom to the top of the pyramid. So they do not show their true length on the plan view.

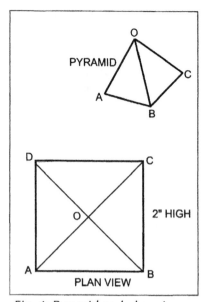

Fig. 4: Pyramid and plan view

You can find the true length of line AO in the same way as finding the length of the 2 x 4—draw a side view of it and then measure the line. Figure 5 shows how this is done. The pyramid is 2" high, so line AO rises a vertical distance of 2". The bottom line of the triangle in Fig. 5 is the length taken from the plan view. (Use your dividers to transfer this length.) The slanted line of the triangle in Fig. 5 is the true length of line AO.

That's all there is to finding true lengths:

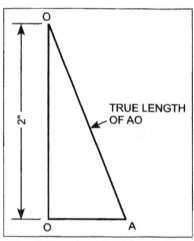

Fig. 5: True length of line AO

- ❑ Draw the side view with the horizontal distance and the vertical distance that a line travels.

- ❑ Draw in the third side of the triangle and measure the true length of the line.

# TRIANGULATING

Now you can learn how to **triangulate**:

- ❑ To triangulate means to work from two known points to locate a third point.

Fig. 6: Start of pyramid pattern

Once the true lengths of an object are found, the pattern is developed by triangulating from points. For example, you can triangulate to develop the pattern for one side of the pyramid—side ABO.

Look back at the plan view in Fig. 4. Line AB is a true length on the plan view because it is on a horizontal plane, so you know the length of AB. Draw this line to start the pattern (Fig. 6). (Use your dividers to transfer the length.) The true length of line AO (and therefore line BO) has been determined (Fig. 5). Before you can draw in these lines, you need to know where point O is. Find this by measuring from points A and B. Set dividers to the true length of AO (from Fig. 5). With A as the center point, swing an arc in the area where point O will be (Fig. 7). Since AO and BO are the same length, swing the same arc from point B. The intersection of these arcs establishes point O. Draw lines AO and BO (Fig. 8) and the pattern for side ABO is established.

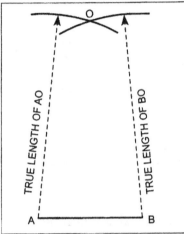

Fig. 7: Swing arcs from A and B to find O

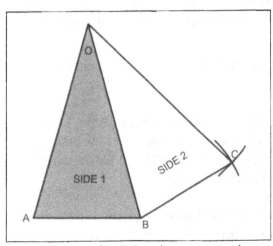

Fig. 8: When side ABO is drawn, triangulate to find point C

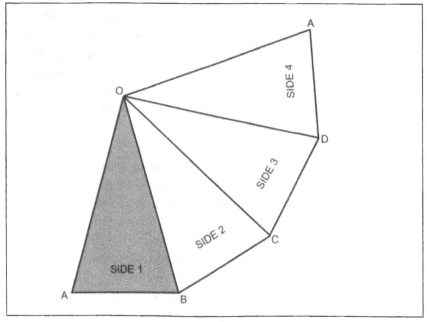

*Fig. 9: Complete pattern for the pyramid*

The second side of the pyramid pattern (side BCO) can be drawn in the same way. Points B and O are now the known points. Triangulate from them to locate point C (Fig. 8):

- ❏ Set dividers to distance BC from the plan view and swing an arc from point B.
- ❏ Set dividers to the true length of CO (it's the same length as AO and BO) and swing an arc from point O.
- ❏ The intersection of these two arcs establishes point C.

The other two sides of the pattern are found in the same way. Use points C and O as the known points to establish point D (Fig. 9). Then use point D and O to locate point A, which completes the pattern (Fig. 9).

Note that this pattern was developed as viewed from the outside. This was done to make it easier for you to understand the process. In practice, sheet metal patterns are almost always developed as seen from the inside.

# ELEVATION VIEWS

In laying out duct patterns you usually deal with plan views. However, recognize that the same principles of true lengths apply to elevation (side) views. On an elevation view, you are seeing lines on a vertical plane. Lines that lie on a vertical plane are true lengths on the drawing. A line that slants toward or away from you is not a true length and you have to draw a side view of it and measure its true length.

# SUMMARY

So there you have it—that's all there is to triangulation:

- ❑ Decide which lines on a drawing are true lengths and which are not.

- ❑ To find the true lengths, draw true views of the lines and measure them.

- ❑ To develop the pattern by triangulation, **work from two points you know to locate a third point**.

# 4  RECTANGULAR TRANSITIONS

**Transitions** are needed in almost every duct run to change the size or shape of the ductwork. This chapter explains how to lay out rectangular transitions.

## 2-PIECE TRANSITION

A duct run is often kept flat on the top to keep it against the overhead. A transition is also likely to be flat on top. If the duct is relatively small and the change is only in the height of the duct, such as a 12 × 12 duct changing to a 12 × 6 duct (Fig. 1), the transition is often made in two pieces. A **2-piece transition** can be cut out of a sheet economically and has only two seams.

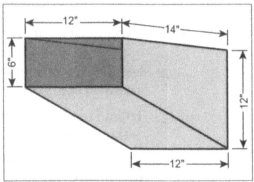

Fig. 1: Transition—flat on top

Figure 2 shows the layout for the 2-piece transition shown in Fig. 1. The finished fitting is 14" long, but the bottom piece is longer than this. This is because it must be long enough to fit the slanted side of the fitting. Use dividers or a rule to transfer dimension X from the slanted side of the pattern to the straight bottom piece pattern.

Of course, allowances for seams and connections have to be added to make a complete pattern.

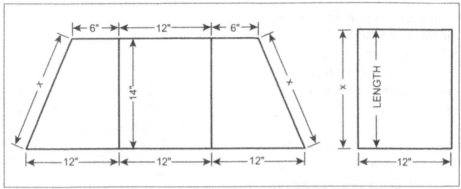

*Fig. 2: Patterns for 2-piece transition flat on top, in Fig. 1*

# 4-PIECE TRANSITION

More often, transitions are made in four pieces in order to save both time and sheet metal. Figure 3 shows the plan and elevation of a typical **4-piece transition**. Each side of this transition is different. You must learn how to lay out these transitions and how to check your layouts by matching sides.

Always lay out the patterns for each side so that the inside is the side you see. This is so the marking instructions for forming will be on the inside of the fitting when it is finished. Also, it is less confusing if you see all the patterns from the same side. To lay out the patterns with the inside up, picture yourself as being inside the fitting and looking at the side. You can then visualize whether an edge slants to the left or to the right.

The length of the finished fitting in Fig. 3 is 6½", but

*Fig. 3: 4-piece transition*

none of the patterns will be 6½" long. Because each side slants, the length of each pattern piece will be determined by the true length of the centerline of that side.

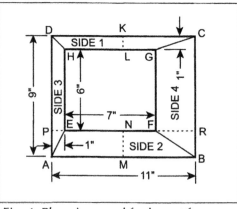

Figure 4 shows a plan view of the fitting marked to explain the layout. Each side is identified by a number. The corners are identified with letters.

*Fig. 4: Plan view used for layout for 4-piece transition*

# Lay Out Side 1

To lay out side 1:

- ❏ Draw a true length triangle (Fig. 5A) to determine the true length of the centerline (KL) of Side 1 in Fig. 4. Since the fitting is 6½" (Fig. 3), the true length triangle is 6½" high. Since this side slants in 1", draw a 1" side on the true length triangle (A in Fig. 5). The third side of the triangle is the true length of line KL. By measurement on the triangle the true length is found to be 6⁹⁄₁₆".

- ❏ To start the layout, draw the bottom of side 1 at 11" (Fig. 5A). This is line DC in the plan view (Fig. 4). Note that D is marked on the left end of the line, since you want to see the inside of the pattern.

- ❏ Square up a line from point D to provide a line to measure from.

- ❏ Draw a line parallel to line DC and 6⁹⁄₁₆" above it (the true length of side 1).

- ❏ Measure over 1" from the square line to establish point H, because side 3 slants in 1".

- ❏ From point H, measure 7" to establish point G, because the top opening is 7" on Side 1.

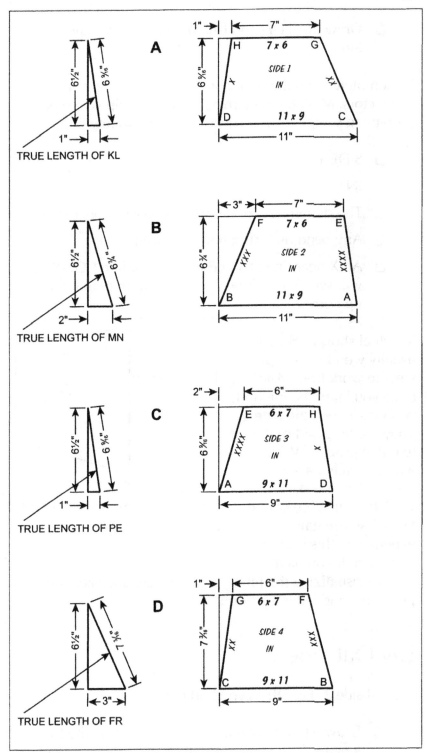

*Fig. 5: Patterns for 4-piece transition in Fig. 3*

❏ Draw lines DH and CG to complete the layout of Side 1.

To complete the pattern, add allowances for seams and connectors. Mark the pattern as shown to help you keep everything straight in your head. Mark the following:

❏ SIDE 1

❏ IN

❏ The dimensions of the top and bottom openings

❏ Any bending instructions required

❏ An X near line DH and an XX near line CG. (You will see in a bit how they are helpful in matching up corners.)

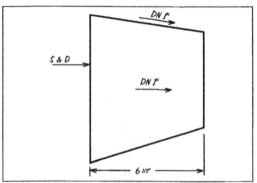

Fig. 6: Shop ticket for Fig. 3 transition

In actual shop work, you usually won't have a plan view to work from. And once you learn the method, you won't need the letters. They are only part of the learning process. What you will generally have is a shop ticket or a sketch to work from like the one in Fig. 6. As you gain experience, this is all you will need. If you have trouble visualizing the fitting, make a freehand sketch of the plan view and letter the corners.

## Lay Out Side 2

Lay out side 2 (Fig 5B) as you laid out side 1:

❏ Draw a true length triangle to determine the true length of the centerline MN. Calculation shows that side 2 slants in 2":

$$9" - (6" + 1") = 2"$$

The third side of the triangle is the true length of MN (by measurement, 6¾") (Fig. 5B).

- [ ] To start the layout, draw the bottom of side 2 at 11" (line BA). B is on the left end to make the inside of the pattern up.
- [ ] Square up a line from point B to provide a line to measure from.
- [ ] Draw a line parallel to line BA and 6¾" above it (the true length of side 2).
- [ ] Measure over 3" from the square line to establish point F, because side 4 slants in 3":

$$11" - (7" + 1") = 3"$$

- [ ] From point F, measure 7" to establish point E, because the top opening is 7".
- [ ] Draw lines BF and AE to complete the layout (Fig. 5B).

Add allowances for seams and connections. Mark the pattern. Add XXX near edge BF and XXXX near edge AE.


# Lay Out Sides 3 and 4

The patterns for sides 3 (Fig. 5C) and 4 (Fig. 5D) are laid out in the same way. Add the X marks as shown.

# Check the Patterns

You won't have the corner letters on your pattern (they are just for explanation), so use the X marks of the edges to check the patterns and make sure the mating edges will fit together:

- ❑ A single X was marked on edge DH on side 1 and edge DH on side 3. These two edges must fit together, so they must be the same length. If they are not, one of the patterns is wrong.

- ❑ Edge CG on side 1 and CG on side 4 are marked XX. Check to see if these are the same length.

- ❑ Check edges BF and AE in the same way.

The X marks can also be used to avoid confusion when the fitting is assembled. The two edges with XXXX must be assembled together, the two edges with XXX must be assembled together, and so on.

# S OFFSETS

**5**

**Offsets** are used to move ductwork around an obstruction. An offset may also act as a transition, to change the duct size as well as to offset. The **S offset** (Fig. 1) is probably the most commonly used offset. An S offset is preferred to a straight transition (described in Chapter 4) because it provides a smoother flow of air.

## STANDARD S OFFSET

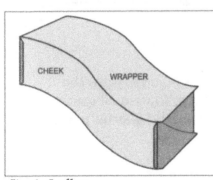

Fig. 1: S offset

A **standard S offset** has the same size duct on both ends. (This is a basic layout and all the more complicated S offsets are based on it.) The **cheeks** (Fig. 1) are the sides of the S offset with curved edges. The **wrappers** (Fig. 1) are the sides of the offset that are formed to fit the S curves of the offset.

## Cheek Pattern

Use the following steps to lay out the cheek of a standard offset with the dimensions shown in Fig. 2. Letters are added to

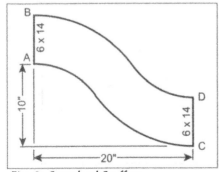

Fig. 2: Standard S offset

Fig. 2 so that you can follow the layout more easily.

❏ **Step 1.** Locate the corners (A, B, C, D) of the cheek. Then mark the **center points** of each end (E and F).

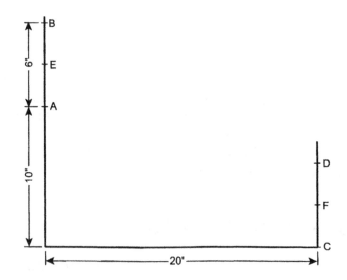

❏ **Step 2.** From center points E and F, draw the **centerline** and divide it into four equal spaces. The dividing marks G and H are the **quarter points**.

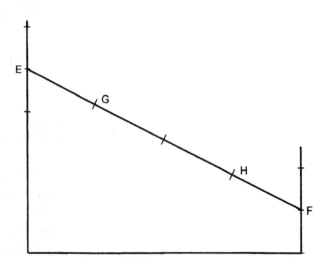

❏ **Step 3.** From the quarter points G and H, lines are squared up as shown until they intersect the end lines at J and K.

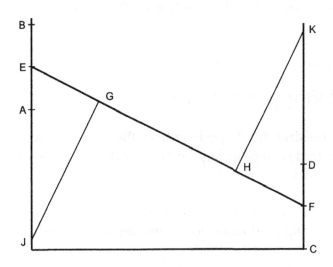

❏ **Step 4.** Use J as a center and swing arcs from B and A. Use K as a center and swing arcs from D and C.

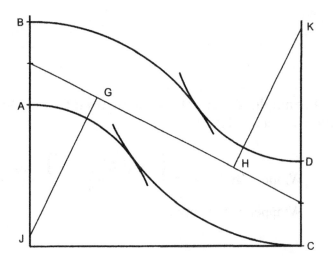

If your layout is accurate, the arcs will join to make a smooth S curve. In actual shop practice, the arcs sometime miss slightly. Don't take time to do a new layout. Just sketch in a smooth curve to make them join. Of course allowance must be added for seams and connections.

## Wrapper Pattern

The **stretchout** (the length) of the wrapper pattern can be found by measuring the curve with a flexible rule or a strip of metal.

However, instead of measuring the curve, you can use the following equation to determine the stretchout:

$$\text{Wrapper stretchout} = \frac{\left(4 \times \sqrt{O^2 + L^2}\right) - L}{3}$$

O—Amount of offset
L—Length of offset

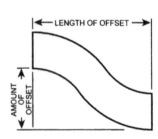

For example, the equation can be used to find the length of the wrapper in Fig. 2:

$$\text{Wrapper stretchout} = \frac{\left(4 \times \sqrt{10^2 + 20^2}\right) - 20}{3}$$

$$\text{Wrapper stretchout} = 23.148 \ (23\,\tfrac{1}{8}")$$

# S OFFSET THAT CHANGES SIZE IN THE CHEEK

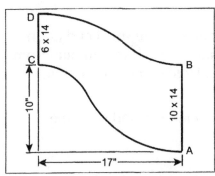

*Fig. 3: S offset that changes sizes in the check*

Figure 3 shows an offset that changes size in the cheek. The width for the wrappers does not change—the wrappers are 14" on each end.

## Cheek Pattern

The layout for the cheek for this fitting is the same as the standard S offset except that there are **two** centerlines. If effect, you are putting a slice of metal down the center of the cheek to make up the difference in the end widths.

❑ **Step 1.** Locate the corners (A, B, C, D) of the cheek.

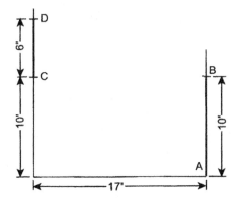

❏ **Step 2.** Draw the two **centerlines** and mark the **quarter points**.

> ❏ Locate the center point for the small end (point E).
>
> ❏ Take **half** the length of the small end (3" in this example) and measure this amount from each side of the large end to locate points F and G.
>
> ❏ Draw the two centerlines and mark the quarter points.

This operation puts a space (EFG) down the middle of the cheek to make up for the difference in sizes.

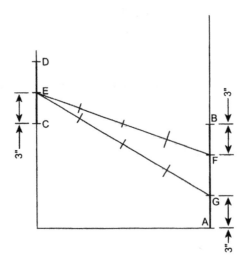

❏ **Step 3.** For each of the centerlines, square up lines from the quarter points.

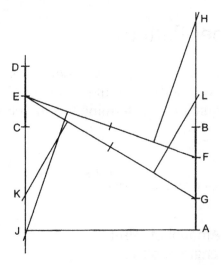

The intersection of the squared lines and the end lines establishes the center points for the arcs.

❑ **Step 4.** Swing the arcs.
Use the correct center point for each arc:

    ❑ The squared lines from the **top centerline** provide the centers (H and J) for the **top arcs**.

    ❑ The squared lines from the **bottom centerline** provide the centers (K and L) for the **bottom arcs**.

The arcs should meet. If the arcs miss by a large amount, your layout is wrong and you probably used the wrong center point for an arc.

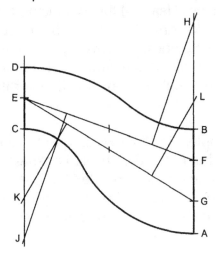

# Wrapper Pattern

For the stretchout of each wrapper pattern, measure around the curve with a flexible rule or a strip of metal. Or you can use the equation to determine the stretchout:

$$\text{Wrapper stretchout} = \frac{\left(4 \times \sqrt{O^2 + L^2}\right) - L}{3}$$

O—Amount of offset
L—Length of offset

AMOUNT OF OFFSET

AMOUNT OF OFFSET

←— LENGTH OF OFFSET —→

The stretchout of the two wrappers will be different because the offset of the two curves are different. The offset of the **bottom curve** is 10" (Fig. 3). The overall dimension to the back of the small side is 16" (10" + 6" = 16"). Therefore the offset of the **top curve** is 6" (16" – 10" = 6").

## S OFFSET THAT CHANGES SIZE IN THE WRAPPER

You have now learned the two methods of laying out S offset cheeks. Any cheek for an S offset can be laid out by these two methods. However, you will encounter S offsets that change size in the wrapper. These are still the same basic layout, but you have to allow for the true length of the slanted side.

For example, Fig. 4 shows an offset that changes size in the wrapper but not in the cheek. Looking at the plan view it is obvious that the slanted side (A'C') has to be longer than the flat side (AC). (In actual practice, you do not need the plan view—it is shown for clarification.)

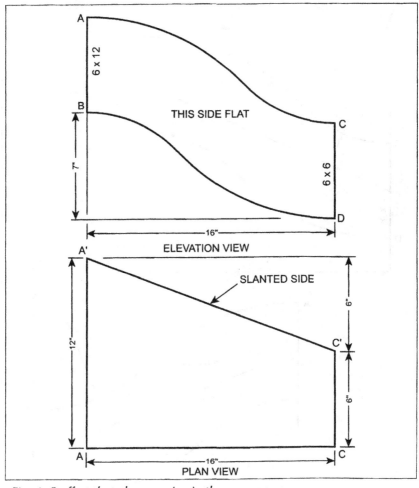

*Fig. 4: S offset that changes size in the wrapper*

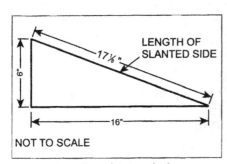

*Fig. 5: True length triangle for length of slanted cheek*

To find the length of the slanted side, draw the true length triangle (Fig. 5). The 16" is the length of the finished offset and 6" is amount that the side slants in. Measuring on the true length triangle shows that the length of the slanted cheek is 17⅛".

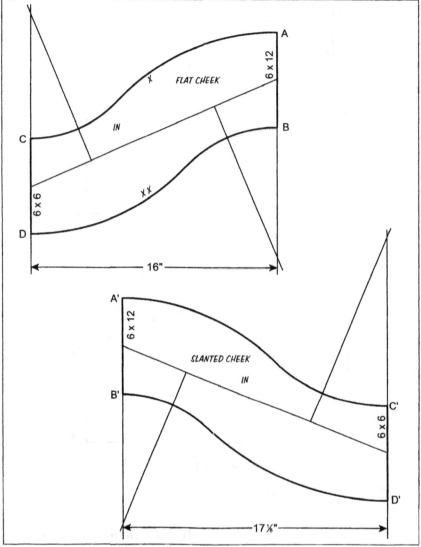

*Fig. 6: Check patterns for Fig. 4 offset*

## Cheek Patterns

Two standard S offset cheeks need to be laid out (Fig. 6):

- ☐ The flat cheek is 16" long.
- ☐ The slanted cheek is 17⅛" long.

Lay out these cheeks as you would for a standard S offset. Mark these two patterns for IN and for size as soon as they are laid out. It is easy to get them mixed up.

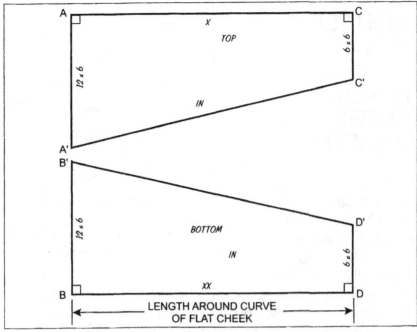

*Fig. 7: Wrapper patterns for Fig. 4 offset*

The letters on Figs. 4, 6, and 7 are not necessary for layout. They are added so that you can more easily see how the patterns are related.

## Wrapper Pattern

The two wrapper patterns (Fig. 7) have the same dimensions.

To lay out the **top wrapper** (Fig. 7), measure the length of the **curve of the flat cheek** and draw line CA. Square 6" from C and 12" from A. Then draw the slanted side. Line C'A' will be the correct length for the curve of the slanted side. Check your layout by seeing if line C'A' on your wrapper is the same as the curve of the slanted cheek.

The **bottom wrapper** (Fig. 7) will be the same except that the IN side of the pattern will be the opposite side.

The X and XX on the cheek patterns (Fig. 6) and on the wrapper patterns (Fig. 7) are guides for match-up during assembly.

48

# S OFFSET THAT CHANGES IN BOTH CHEEK AND WRAPPER

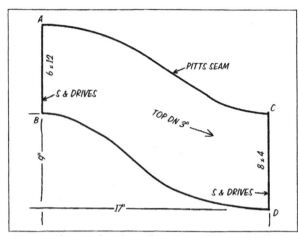

Figure 8 shows a shop ticket for an S offset that changes in the cheek and on both sides of the wrapper. Generally, this is the

*Fig. 8: Shop ticket for offset that changes in the cheek and both sides of the wrapper*

information you will be provided. Note the marking **TOP DN 3"** with an **arrow**. This shows that the cheek drops (slants) a total of 3" in the direction of the 8 × 4 end. (On a shop ticket, the side you see is called the **top** even though it may be on the side when it is installed.)

Usually you can figure mentally how much the other cheek drops (slants). If you cannot see it right away, sketch a plan view like the one in Fig. 9. Then you can see that the back cheek drops 5". This means that the cheeks will be different lengths because they drop different amounts.

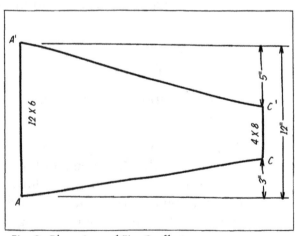

*Fig. 9: Plan view of Fig. 8 offset*

The letters A, B, C, and D on Figs. 8, 9, 10, 11, and 12 are not needed for layout. Use them to help you see how the patterns fit together.

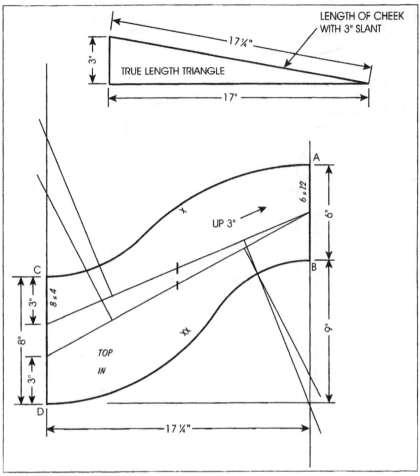

*Fig. 10: Layout of front cheek for Fig. 8 offset*

## Cheek Patterns

Find the length of the **front cheek** with a true length triangle (Fig. 10). (One leg of the triangle is 3" because the cheek drops 3".) The true length triangle shows that the length of the front cheek will be 17¼". It is laid out like any S offset cheek that changes size (Fig. 10). The ³⁄₁₆" edge for the Pittsburgh (not shown here) is swung at the same time as the curves. In actual practice, the inside curve is not usually marked.

Next find the length of the **back cheek**, which drops 5". The true length triangle (Fig. 11) shows that the length of the back cheek will be 17¾". The back cheek (Fig. 11) is laid

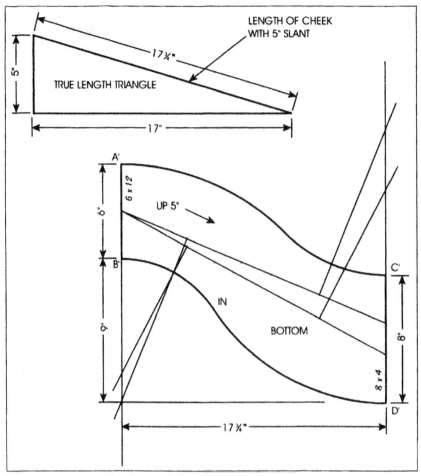

*Fig. 11: Layout of back cheek for Fig. 8 offset*

out the same way as the front cheek. Of course allowances for seams and connections have to be added.

Note that both patterns are marked for the inside, with the end dimensions given. One cheek is marked with X and XX, to be matched with X and XX on the wrappers. This cuts down the chances for error when the offset is assembled.

## Wrapper Patterns

To lay out the wrapper patterns, measure the two curves of the front cheek. Measure the inside curve of the pattern—not the edge of the allowance. The lengths of the two curves determine the lengths of the wrappers.

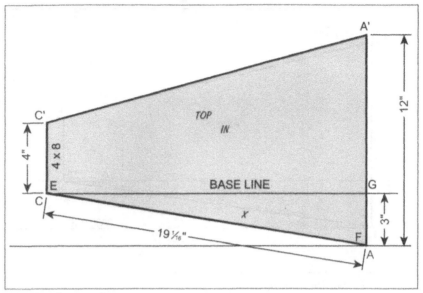

*Fig. 12: Pattern for top wrapper*

To lay out the **top wrapper** (Fig. 12), use these steps:

- ❏ Measure the top curve on the front cheek pattern. The top curve in Fig. 10 measures $19\frac{1}{16}$".

- ❏ Draw a base line a little longer than $19\frac{1}{16}$". Mark point E on the left end of the line so that the pattern will be IN. Square up a line from point E for one end line of the layout.

- ❏ Draw a second line parallel to the base line and 3" below it (the amount the side will slant in).

- ❏ Hold the end of a rule on point E and move it until the $19\frac{1}{16}$" mark touches the second line. This is point F. Line EF is the proper length to fit the curve of the cheek ($19\frac{1}{16}$").

- ❏ From point F, erect a line that is square to line EG. This establishes the other end line for the pattern.

- ❏ On the end line from point F, measure up 12". On the end line from point E, measure up 4". Then draw line C' A'.

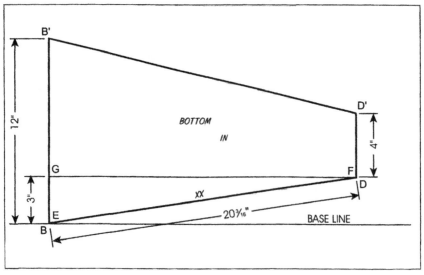

*Fig. 13: Layout for bottom wrapper*

This completes the basic pattern for the top wrapper. Add allowances for seams and connections. Mark the pattern IN and mark the dimensions of each end. Mark an X on the edge that will fit with the X on the cheek pattern.

The letters are not needed on actual layout. They are used here so that you can follow the explanation of the process.

Develop the patterns for the **bottom wrapper** in the same way (Fig. 13):

- ❏ Measure the bottom curve of the front cheek pattern. The bottom curve in Fig. 10 measures 19⅝".

- ❏ Draw a base line a little longer than 20³⁄₁₆". Mark point E on the left end of the line. Square up a line from point E for one end line of the pattern.

- ❏ Draw a second line parallel to the base line and 3" above it (the amount the side will drop).

- ❏ Hold the end of a rule on point E and move it until the 20³⁄₁₆" mark touches the second line. This is point F.

- ❑ From point F, erect a line that is square to line FG. This establishes the other end line of the pattern.

- ❑ On the end line from point E, measure up 12". On the end line from point F, measure up 4". Then draw line D'B'.

This completes the basic pattern for the bottom wrapper. Add allowances for seams and connections. Mark the pattern IN and mark the dimensions of each end. Mark an XX on the edge that will fit with the XX on the cheek pattern.

To make sure your patterns are correct, measure the curves of the slanted cheek to see if they match the lengths of the matching edges of the wrapper patterns. If the lengths vary more than about ⅛" you may have an error in layout.

# 6

# *RECTANGULAR DUCT ELBOWS*

An elbow is probably the most common fitting in duct runs. The different types of elbows and the names they are commonly called are listed below. Like everything in the trade, the names may vary in different areas of the country. Learn the terms used in your area. Elbows are classified in different ways:

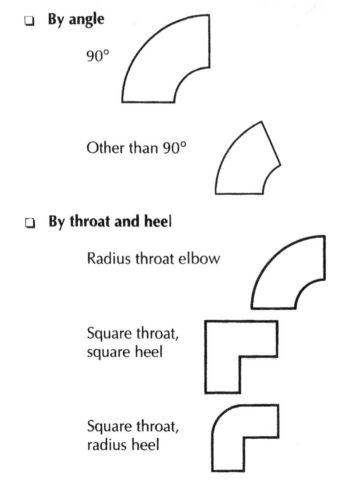

❑ **By angle**

90°

Other than 90°

❑ **By throat and heel**

Radius throat elbow

Square throat, square heel

Square throat, radius heel

## ❏ By change in size or by offset

No change—straight elbow

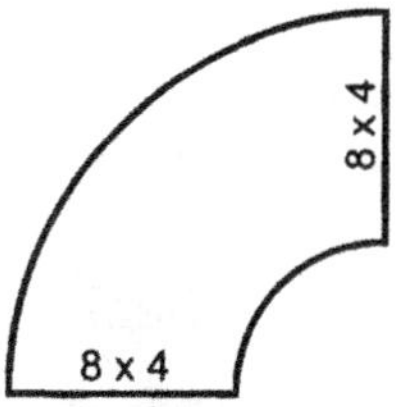

8 x 4
8 x 4

Size change in cheek—
change elbow

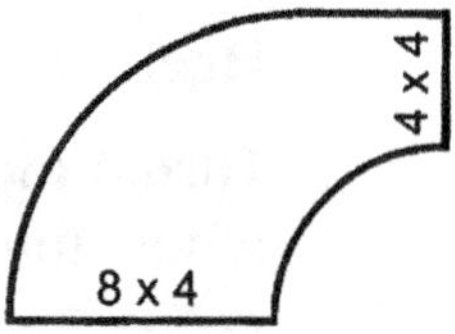

4 x 4
8 x 4

Size change in heel and
throat—transitional elbow

8 x 8
8 x 4

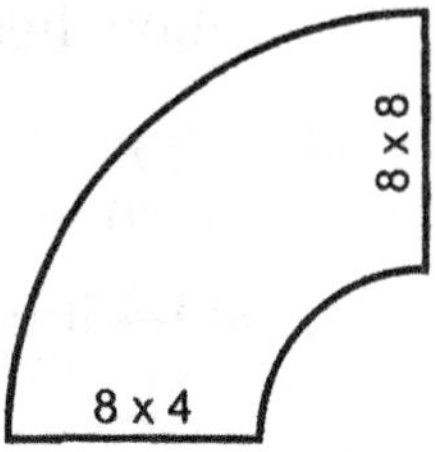

Size change in cheek as well
as heel and throat—
transitional elbow

4 x 8
8 x 4

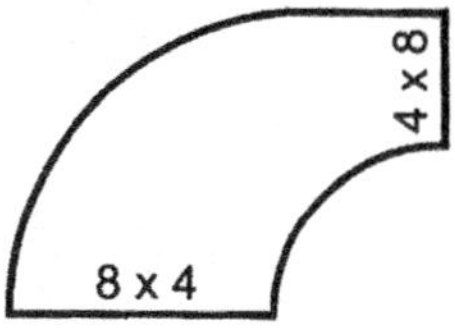

Offset elbow

Offset and size change

This sounds like a great deal to learn, but—like most things in layout work—there are only a few basic principles to learn and these are applied in different ways.

# TERMS

Make sure you know these terms used for rectangular duct elbows (Fig. 1):

- **Cheek**—The flat side of the elbow.

- **Throat**—The side that forms the inside of the elbow.

- **Heel**—The side that forms the outside of the elbow.

- **Throat radius**—The radius of the arc that forms the elbow throat.

- **Heel radius**—The radius of the arc that forms the elbow heel.

- **Drop**—The amount an elbow cheek slants up or down from one end to the other.

- **SO**—Stretchout of a pattern

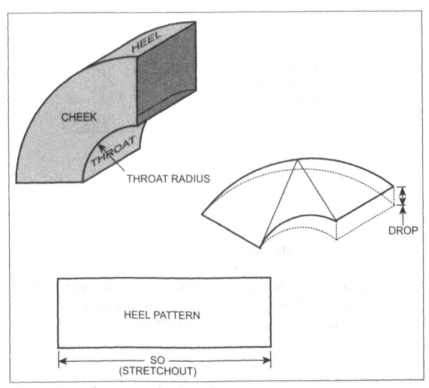

*Fig. 1: Terms for rectangular duct elbows*

# RADIUS THROAT ELBOWS
## Straight Elbow

An elbow with the same dimensions on each end is called a **straight elbow**. To lay out the cheek for the 90° straight elbow in Fig. 2, follow these steps:

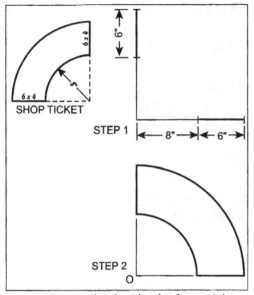

*Fig. 2: Layout for the cheek of a straight elbow*

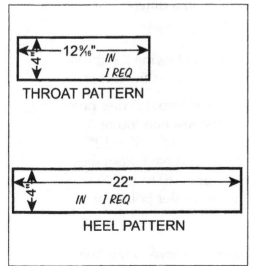

*Fig. 3: Heel and throat patterns, without seam and edge allowances*

❏ Step 1—Draw a 90° corner and establish the corner points of the elbow (Fig. 2).

❏ Step 2—Use the corner point (O) as the center and swing the throat radius and the heel radius (Fig. 2).

Of course allowances must be added for seams and connections.

Next determine the stretchout (SO) for the heel and throat patterns (Fig. 3) with one of these methods:

❏ Method 1—Measure the curves with a flexible rule or strip of metal.

❏ Method 2—Use a calculator and this equation:

Stretchout = 1.57 × Radius

For example, calculate the throat stretchout for the elbow in Fig. 2:

Throat SO = 1.57 × Radius

Throat SO = 1.57 x 8

Throat SO = 12.56 (12%₆")

Calculate the stretchout for the heel in Fig. 2:

Heel SO = 1.57 × Radius

Heel SO = 1.57 x (8 + 6)

Heel SO = 21.98 (22")

NOTE: If you do not know how to convert a decimal to 16ths of an inch, see Chapter 1, pages 9-10.

## Change Elbow

An elbow that changes size in the cheek only is called a **change elbow** (Fig. 4). For this type of elbow, two center points are needed—one for the throat and a different one for the heel. To lay out the cheek for Fig. 4:

❑ Step 1—Draw a square corner and swing the throat radius with O as center (Fig. 4). This is the throat.

❑ Step 2—Set the dividers from the throat center point (O) to the heel point of the smallest end (point A). For this elbow, the distance is 12" (6" + 6" = 12"). Use the divider setting (12") to step back from the heel point of the largest side (point B) to locate point O′ (Fig. 4). Use O′ as the center point and swing the heel radius.

Square a line from A to meet the curve of the heel radius.

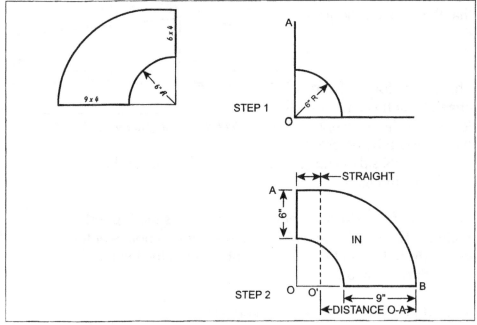

Fig. 4: A change elbow changes in the cheek only

When you make the other cheek, make sure you mark the correct IN side so that it is formed and assembled correctly.

## Transitional Elbow that Changes in Heel and Throat

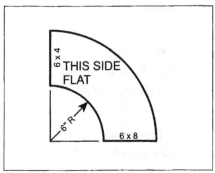

Fig. 5: A transitional elbow changes in the heel and throat

Elbows that change size in the heel and throat are called **transitional elbows** or **drop cheek elbows**. The cheek for these elbows slants in or out. Therefore the layout of the cheek requires triangulation to allow for the additional lengths required by the slant.

Figure 5 is an elbow that changes in the heel and throat. Note that the front cheek is flat. This means

that the back cheek drops
4"
(8" − 4" = 4").

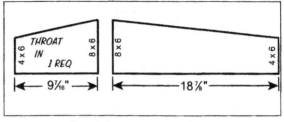

The pattern for the **front cheek** (which is flat) looks like Fig. 5 except

Fig. 6: Heel and throat patterns for Fig. 5

that is would be reversed so that the IN side is up. The patterns for the heel and throat are shown in Fig. 6.

The layout for the **drop cheek** commonly uses the **6-point method**. The 6 points (Fig. 7A) are the four end points of the cheek (A, B, C, and D) and midpoints around the heel and throat curve (E and F).

To start the pattern for the drop cheek:

- ❏ Draw the cheek as if it were flat (Fig. 7A). Note that it is positioned so that the inside is up.

- ❏ Label the corners as points A, B, C, and D. Locate the midpoints E and F (Fig. 7A). These midpoints must be exactly halfway around the heel and throat curves. Use your dividers to locate the midpoint.

- ❏ Draw the layout lines shown in Fig. 7A. As you gain experience, you will not draw these lines, because only the distances are needed, not the lines.

- ❏ Use true length triangles (Fig. 7B) to find the true lengths of the layout lines on the slanted side:

  - ❏ Only lines BE, AE, and AF have to be determined because lines DE, CE, and CF on the other half of the layout are the same as BE, AE, and AF.

  - ❏ The drop on this cheek is 4". Therefore the drop of the lines to the halfway points is 2" (half the drop).

  - ❏ Lines AB, CD, and FE are true lengths on the drawing. (They are not slanted up or down.) They do not have to be found.

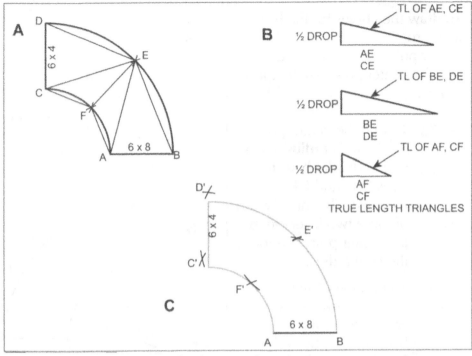

*Fig. 7: Use the 6-point method to lay out a drop cheek*

Develop the pattern of the drop cheek over the flat cheek drawing. Points A and B will be the same. You will need to establish points E', F', C', and D' for the drop cheek:

❏ Locate **new point E'** by triangulating from points A and B (Fig. 7C), using the true lengths of AE and BE (from Fig. 7A) as distances for the arcs.

❏ Locate point F' by triangulating from point A and the new point E' (Fig. 7C). Note that line FE is a true length on the pattern. Since both points F and E are at half the drop, they are at the same level.

❏ Locate point C' by triangulating from E' and F' (Fig. 7C), using the true lengths of line CE and line CF.

❏ Locate point D' by triangulating from C' and E' (Fig. 7C). Line CD is a true length on the pattern because both points have dropped the full amount and therefore are level.

To draw the curves for the heel and throat, you need to find the center point for the heel radius and the center point for the throat radius:

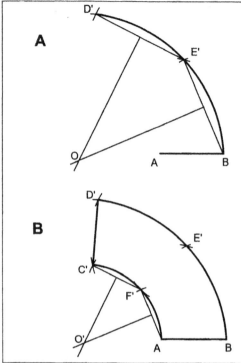

- ❏ To find the center point for the **heel radius**, erect perpendicular bisectors to lines D'E' and E'B (Fig. 8A). The intersection of these two bisectors is the center point (O) for the heel radius.

- ❏ To find the center point for the **throat radius**, erect perpendicular bisectors to lines C'F' and F'A (Fig. 8B). The intersection of these two bisectors is the center point (O') for the throat radius.

*Fig. 8: Finding center points for heel and throat*

You can check to make sure your pattern is correct. The length of heel curve on the cheek should be the same as the slanted edge of the heel pattern. The length of the throat curve on the cheek should be the same as the slanted edge of the throat pattern.

Be sure to add allowances for seams and connections. Mark the IN side.

## Shortcuts

Most shortcuts are simply a matter of eliminating lines. Instead of drawing separate true length triangles, draw them on the flat cheek pattern (Fig. 9). Set dividers at half the drop of the cheek and swing arcs at points E and F. This

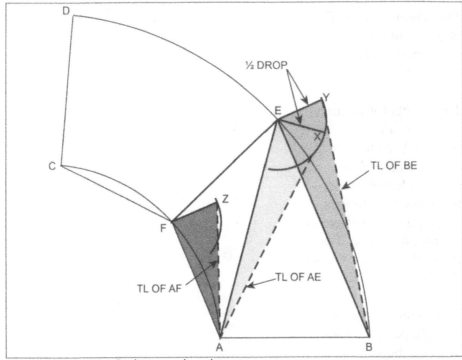

Fig. 9: Shortcut for finding true lengths

establishes the height of the true length triangles. To form the true length triangle for line BE, hold a square on line EB to draw line EY. Set the dividers to distance BY. This is the true length of line BE.

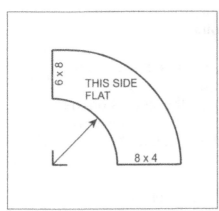

Fig. 10: Transitional elbow that changes size in the cheek as well as the heel and throat

Form the true length triangles for line AE and line AF in the same way.

# Transitional Elbow that Changes in Cheek and Heel and Throat

A transitional elbow can change in the cheek as well as the heel and throat. The elbow in Fig. 10 changes size in the cheek as well as the heel and throat.

The pattern for the flat cheek is like the shop ticket (Fig. 10) but reversed.

The points for the drop cheek are developed (Fig. 11A) as for any transitional elbow cheek. However there are some differences, since part of the heel is a straight section. For example, you can't use dividers to find the true midpoint of the heel. The longer the straight part, the more you will be in error if you just use dividers:

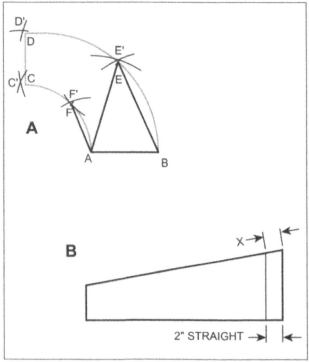

Fig. 11: Developing the pattern for the drop cheek and the heel

❏ To determine the midpoint accurately, first lay out the flat cheek (Fig. 10). Then lay out the pattern for the heel (Fig. 11B). Measure the length of the slanted side on the heel pattern. Take half of this and measure it around the heel of the cheek to locate the midpoint.

The straight section of the drop cheek must be longer than the straight section on the flat cheek since it drops. To determine the length of the straight, mark the straight on the heel pattern and square up a line (Fig. 11B). Distance X is the length of straight on the slanted cheek pattern.

NOTE: The amount of straight on the flat cheek of a transitional elbow cheek is the difference between the two ends. The ends of this elbow cheek are 8" and 6" (Fig. 10). Therefore the straight is 2" (8" - 6" = 2").

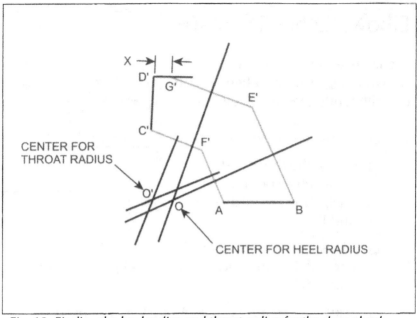

*Fig. 12: Finding the heel radius and throat radius for the drop cheek*

To find the **center point for the heel radius** of the drop cheek:

- From line D'C' (the small end of the cheek) square a line from point D.

- Measure the length of straight on this line to establish point G'. (The amount of straight (X) was shown in Fig. 11B.)

- Erect perpendicular bisectors to lines G'E' and E'B. This establishes point O (Fig. 12) which is the center for the heel radius.

To find the **center point for the throat radius**, erect perpendicular bisectors to lines C'F' and F'A to establish the throat center point O' (Fig. 12).

# Elbows Other Than 90°

A **change elbow less than 90°** is shown in Fig. 13. This cheek is laid out differently than a 90° elbow:

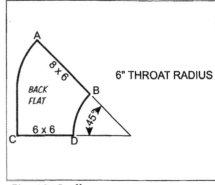

*Fig. 13: S offset*

- [ ] Draw the angle (Fig. 14A).

- [ ] Swing the throat radius from center point O (Fig. 14B). This establishes D and B.

- [ ] Measure the width of both ends of the elbow to establish heel points A and C (Fig. 14C).

- [ ] Square lines from points A and C to establish point X (Fig. 14C).

- [ ] Use point X as a center and swing an arc from point A to locate point Y.

- [ ] From point Y, square a line to line AO.

- [ ] Where this squared line intersects line (AO) is the center point (O') for the heel radius.

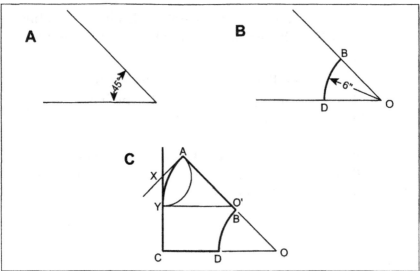

*Fig. 14: Layout for the 45° change elbow in Fig. 13*

If an elbow other than 90° changes size in the heel and throat, the layout is the same as for a 90° transitional elbow.

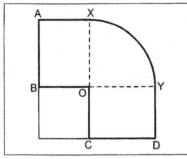

Fig. 15: Square throat radius heel elbow

# SQUARE THROAT ELBOWS

## Square Throat Straight Elbow

Figure 15 shows a square throat, radius heel elbow. It is a **straight elbow**—that is, there is no change in size. The center point for the heel is point O. Lines AX and DY are squared from the end lines.

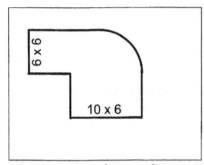

Fig. 16: Square throat radius heel change elbow

## Square Throat Change Elbow

If a square throat, radius heel elbow changes size in the cheek (Fig. 16) the pattern is developed as shown in Fig. 17:

❑ Establish the end points A, B, C, and D (Fig. 17A).

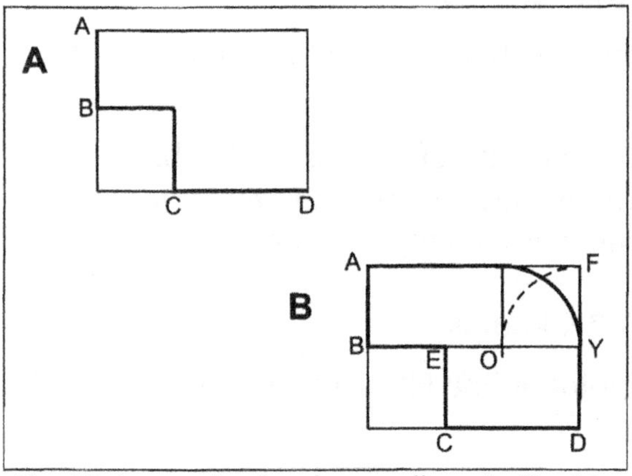

❑ Extend line BE to establish point Y (Fig. 17B).

❑ Set dividers to distance YF. (This is the same as AB, the small end of the cheek.) Use Y as a center and swing an arc from point F to establish point O. This is the center for the heel radius.

Fig. 17: Layout for the change elbow in Fig. 16

# Square Throat Transitional Elbow

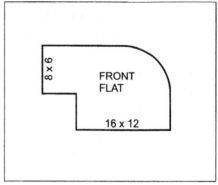

Fig. 18 is a **square throat transitional elbow** that changes size in the heel and throat as well as the cheek. Note that both sides of the throat are the same length. This is done whenever possible because it makes the layout easier.

*Fig. 18: Square throat transitional elbow*

The layout for the drop cheek is basically the same as the 6-point method (Fig. 7) used to lay out the drop cheek for a radius throat transitional elbow.

To lay out the **drop cheek**:

- ❏ Draw the flat cheek (Fig. 19A). Develop the arc for the heel as shown in Fig. 17. Point E is the midpoint of the arc. Draw the layout lines DE, CE, AE, and BE.

- ❏ Draw the throat pattern (Fig. 19B). Mark the bend line (FF′) as shown.

- ❏ Draw the heel pattern (Fig. 19B):

   - ❏ BH is the same length as FA. Add lines GG′ and HH′.

   - ❏ To determine the length of HG, use a flexible rule to measure the arc on the flat cheek. Or you can calculate it with this equation:

     $$Arc = 1.57 \times Radius$$

   - ❏ Find the midpoint of line HG and add line EE′.

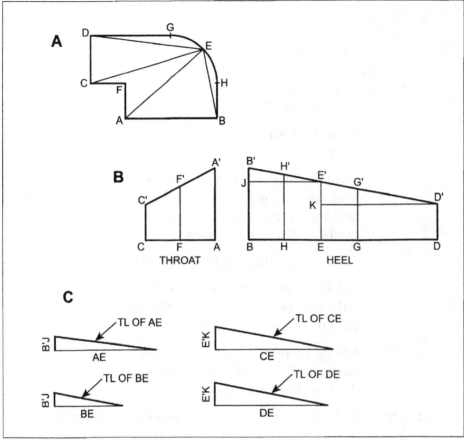

*Fig. 19: Finding true lengths for the drop cheek*

- To determine the amount of drop from E',
  square a line from E' to the end line (point J).
  B'J is the drop for lines AE and BE on the
  cheek. Square a line from D' to line E'E
  (point K). E'K is the drop for lines CE and DE
  on the cheek.

- Draw true length triangles (Fig. 19C) to determine the
  true lengths of the layout lines for the slanted side:

  - The drop for lines AE and BE is B'J. Use this
    as the height of the true length triangles for
    those lines.

  - The drop for lines CE and DE is E'K. Use this
    as the height of the true length triangles for
    those lines.

- ☐ Using the general 6-point method shown in Fig. 7, develop the pattern for the slanted side (Fig. 20), based on the true lengths of the layout lines shown in Fig. 19:

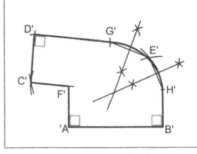

Fig. 20: Developing the layout for the drop side of the transitional square throat elbow

  - ☐ Draw line A′B′ to start the pattern.

  - ☐ Take the distance F′A′ from the throat pattern and square it from A′ to establish F′ on the pattern.

  - ☐ Locate E′ by triangulating from A′ and B′.

  - ☐ Locate C′ by triangulating from F′ and E′. Take the distance F′C′ from the throat pattern.

  - ☐ Locate D′ by triangulating from C′ and E′. Distance C′D′ is the same length as CD on the flat cheek pattern.

- ☐ Develop the heel lines for the slanted cheek pattern (Fig. 20):

  - ☐ Square up a line at B′. Locate H′ by measuring on this line the distance B′H′ from the heel pattern.

  - ☐ Square up a line at D′. Locate G′ by measuring on this line the distance D′G′ from the heel pattern.

- ☐ Develop the **arc** for the heel of the slanted cheek pattern (Fig. 20):

  - ☐ Draw lines G′E′ and E′H′.

  - ☐ Erect bisectors to these lines to establish the center point for the heel radius.

  - ☐ Swing the arc from this center point to complete the slanted cheek pattern.

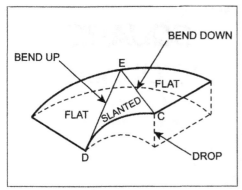

*Fig. 21: Bend lines*

# BEND LINES

**Bend lines** (Fig. 21) are needed on a slanted or offset elbow cheek. This is a matter of **forming** the elbow cheek rather than a **layout process**. Bend lines are important because without them, a slanted or offset cheek pattern will not assemble into a neat elbow.

Bend on lines DE and CE. One bend is down and the other is up, depending on which direction the cheek slants. The amount of bend depends on the amount of drop in the cheek. The first bend gives the throat of the cheek the proper amount of drop. The second bend is the same amount. It throws the end of the elbow back to a flat plane.

# 7

# SQUARE-TO-ROUNDS

**Square-to-round** is a general term for a fitting that has straight lines on one end and a circular form on the other (Fig. 1). Actually, most square-to-rounds are really rectangular to round, but they are still called square-to-rounds.

The patterns for square-to-rounds are developed using triangulation. If you are not sure of how to find true lengths for triangulation, review Chapter 3, Triangulation. As with most layouts, square-to-rounds all use the same basic principles of layout. Once you have learned the basic methods, square-to-rounds are all pretty much the same.

## BASIC LAYOUT

Figure 1 is the plan and elevation of a square-to-round with the circle off-center in one direction. Figure 2 shows how the pattern is developed:

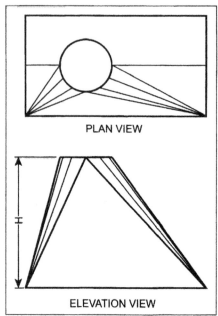

PLAN VIEW

ELEVATION VIEW

Fig. 1: Square-to-round

❑ Draw a full size plan view. Divide the half-circle into 6 equal spaces and draw the layout lines as shown (Fig. 2A).

(Using 6 spaces is

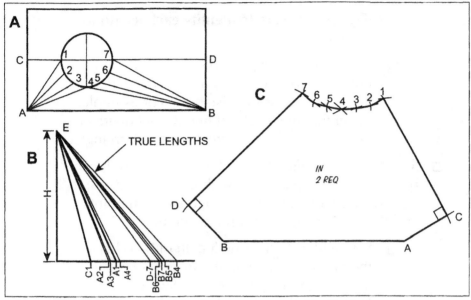

*Fig. 2: Developing the pattern for the square-to-round in Fig. 1*

standard practice, because it is easy to divide the half circle into that number, as explained in Chapter 1. For a very large circle or one with an irregular curve, more spaces might be used. The layout lines are drawn on only half the plan view because the fitting is symmetrical—the other half is the same.)

❏ Letter and number the plan view as shown in Fig. 2A. These letters and numbers will be used on the layout.

(You could use any system of identification, but the way shown is standard practice. Always use the same system to mark square-to-rounds. It makes layout easier.)

❏ Find the true length of every layout line with a true length triangle (Fig. 2B). All the layout lines rise a vertical distance of H (the height of the fitting):

   ❏ Set dividers to the length of each layout line on the plan view and transfer the length to the horizontal line of the true length triangle

(Fig. 2B). **Be sure to identify each length** as shown.

- ❏ In actual practice, the true length lines are not drawn because they are not needed. All that is needed is the distances. For example, to get the true length of line B4, set dividers from E to mark B4 on the true length triangle.

❏ Start the pattern (Fig. 2C) by drawing line AB. It can be picked off the plan view with dividers because it lies on a horizontal plane. Triangulate from points A and B to locate the points on the curve:

- ❏ Set dividers to the true length of B4. This is the distance from E to the mark B4 on the true length triangle (Fig. 2B). Swing an arc from point B on the pattern in the general area where point 4 is expected to be.

- ❏ Set dividers to the true length of A4 (from the true length triangle). Swing an arc from point A on the layout. The intersection of the arcs for B4 and A4 locates point 4 on the layout.

- ❏ Locate point 5 by triangulating from points B and 4. Distance 4-5 is picked off the plan view because it is on a horizontal plane. Distance B5 is from the true length triangle.

- ❏ Locate the rest of the points on the curve by the same method:

  To locate point 6, triangulate from B and 5.
  To locate point 7, triangulate from B and 6.
  To locate point 3, triangulate from A and 4.
  To locate point 2, triangulate from A and 3.
  To locate point 1, triangulate from A and 2.

❏ Locate points D and C. (Up to this point, you have a half-pattern of the circle, but only a quarter pattern of the square. You need points D and C to establish the area called the **wings**.)

- ❏ To locate point D, triangulate from B and 7. Distance BD is picked off the plan view. Distance D7 is from the true length triangle.

- ❏ To locate point C, triangulate from A and 1. Distance AC is picked off the plan view. Distance C1 is from the true length triangle.

This completes the half-pattern for the square-to-round. Add allowances for seams and connections, and mark the pattern. The other half-pattern is also marked from this. The two halves are formed and seamed to form the fitting.

# Check Your Pattern

Here are ways to check that your pattern is correct:

- ❏ The curve for the circle will always be a smooth curve. If any point in your layout of the curve makes an abrupt change from a smooth curve, check your layout.

- ❏ The wings are almost always a 90° angle. If angles BD7 and AC1 are 90° on the plan view (and they usually are), then these same angles on the pattern must be 90° (Fig. 2C). If they are not, the pattern is wrong.

# Shortcut for Finding True Lengths

Figure 3 shows a common method of finding true lengths easily. Only one true length is shown to simplify the explanation:

- ❏ Extend line AC and measure the height of the fitting (H) on it.

- ❏ To find the true length of line A2, use A as a center and swing an arc from point 2 down to the base line AB. This transfers distance A2 down to the horizontal line of the true length triangle. The true length of line A2 is the distance E2'.

Locate A3 and A4 on the base line in the same way. Locate B4, B5, B6, and B7 by swinging an arc from point B. Measure the true lengths from E or E'.

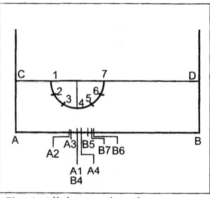

Fig. 3: Shortcut for a true length

Figure 4 shows how this method would actually look as done by an experienced layout person. The arcs and layout lines are not drawn. In order to avoid confusion, it is very important that each point on the horizontal line of the true length triangle be numbered when it is located.

Fig. 4: All the true lengths

# Shortcut for Laying Out Wings with a Square

On the plan view in A in Fig. 2, angles AC1 and BD7 are 90° corners. This means that the same corners on the pattern will be 90°. Therefore, after points 1 and 7 are located, the wings can be drawn using a square, as shown in Fig. 5. Lay the square so that BD is the required length (6" in this illustration) and the blade of the square runs through point 7. Draw lines BD and D7 to form the wing.

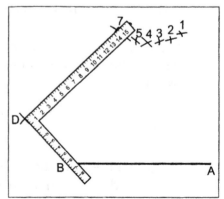

Fig. 5: Laying out the wings by using a square

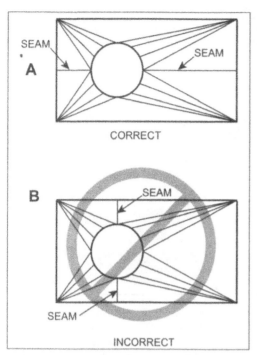

Fig. 6: Locate seam lines to make
symmetrical halves

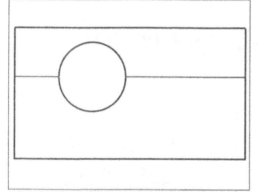

Fig. 7: If the fitting is not symmetrical, the
two halves are laid out separately

A good check on your layout
is to find the true length of
line D7 and see if D7 on the
pattern is that length. If it is
not, your layout is wrong.
The same is true for A1.

## SEAMS

Try to locate seam lines on a
square-to-round so that the
plan view is divided into two
symmetrical halves. A
square-to-round with the
seams properly located is
shown in Fig. 6A. Only half
of the pattern need be laid
out because the other half is
the same. If the seam lines
were located as shown in
Fig. 6B, the two halves of the
fitting would have to be laid
out separately.

In some unusual fittings,
such as the one in Fig. 7, it is
not possible to divide the
plan into symmetrical halves.
In this case, both halves are
laid out separately.

## CENTERED SQUARE-TO-ROUND

A centered **square-to-round** has the circle centered in the
square or rectangle (Fig. 8). Since all four quarters of the
plan view are the same, only a quarter of the plan view, as

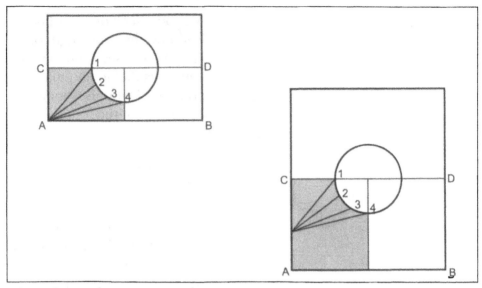

*Fig. 8: Centered square-to-rounds*

shown by the shaded area, needs to be drawn. All the other true lengths are the same.

## SQUARE-TO-ROUND ON A PITCH

Sometimes the square is at an angle to the round (Fig. 9). Another way of saying this is that the round lies on a horizontal plane, while the square is on a pitched plane. This type is called a **square-to-round on a pitch**.

Layout for a square-to-round on a pitch mostly follows basic layout (Fig. 10):

❑ Draw the plan view and establish the layout lines (Fig. 10A).

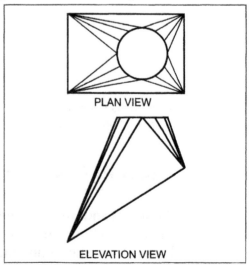

PLAN VIEW

ELEVATION VIEW

*Fig. 9: Square-to-round on a pitch*

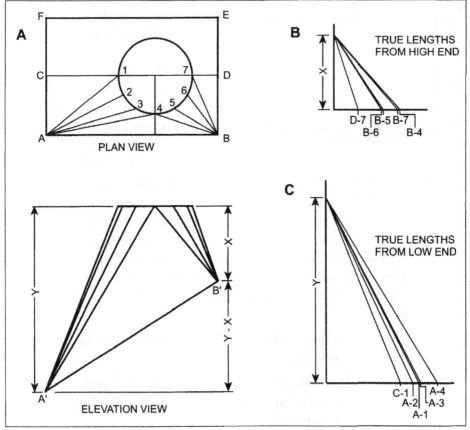

*Fig. 10: True lengths for square-to-round on a pitch*

❏ Letter and number the points.

❏ Find the true lengths of the layout lines. However, you cannot use a single height for the true length triangles:

> ❏ The lines from points B and E are rising the distance X as shown on the elevation view. The true lengths of these lines are found as shown in Fig. 10B, True lengths from the high end.

> ❏ The lines from points A and F are rising the distance Y as shown on the elevation view. The true lengths of these lines are shown in Fig. 10C, True lengths from the low end.

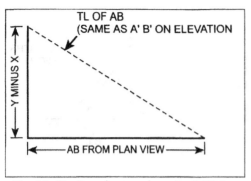

*Fig. 11: Finding the true length of AB for the square-to-round in Fig. 10*

❏ Make the pattern by triangulating from two points to find a third.

Make sure you use the true length of AB to start the layout. Line AB on the plan view is not a true length, because it is on a slanted plane. You can take the true length of line AB from the **elevation view** (Fig. 10). Another way to find the true length of AB is to draw the true length triangle shown in Fig. 11:

❏ The horizontal line is taken from AB in the plan view.

❏ The vertical line of the triangle is the vertical distance that AB rises, which is the distance of Y minus X.

To develop the pattern (Fig. 12):

❏ Draw the true length of line AB.

❏ To locate point 4, triangulate from A and B.

❏ To locate point 5, triangulate from 4 and B.

❏ Locate all the rest of the points around the half circle by triangulation.

❏ To locate point D, triangulate from points 7 and B, or use a framing square.

❏ To locate point C, triangulate from points 1 and A, or use a framing square.

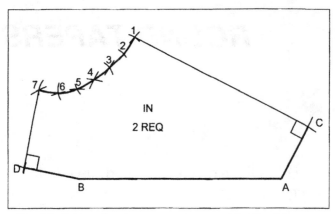

*Fig. 12: Pattern for the square-to-round in Fig. 10*

Note the shape of the pattern in Fig. 12. It is typical of a square-to-round on a pitch and is slightly different from other square-to-round patterns.

# *ROUND TAPERS*

**8**

This chapter describes three different methods used to lay out a round taper:

- ❑ Using three side views—For gradual tapers where great accuracy is not required

- ❑ Sweeping a taper—For centered tapers with a fairly steep taper

- ❑ Triangulation—For any round taper

## TAPER FROM THREE SIDE VIEWS

Figure 1 is a gradual taper that can be developed by **three side views**. This method is accurate enough for most applications. It works only if the taper is centered. To lay out a taper using three side views:

- ❑ Draw a full size side view of the taper (Fig. 2).

- ❑ Attach side views to each side of the first view (Fig. 2). These side views must duplicate the angles as well as the dimensions of the original view. To do this:

  - ❑ Set dividers to the diagonal AD (BC will be the same). Swing this arc from the centers A, B, C, and D.

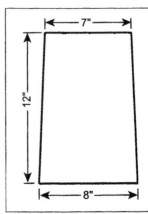

*Fig. 1: Gradual taper*

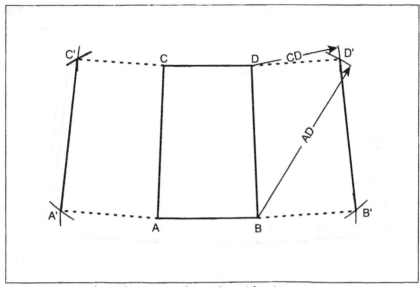

*Fig. 2: Draw the side view and attach 2 side views*

- ❏ Set dividers to distance CD, and swing this arc from D and C. Corner points D' and C' are located where the arcs intersect.

- ❏ Set dividers to distance AB, and swing this arc from A and B. Corner points A' and B' are located where the arcs intersect.

- ❏ Add lines D'B' and C'A'.

❏ Draw arcs through the corner points C', C, D, D' and through A', A, B, B' (Fig. 3). This is usually done by bowing a flexible rule through the points and scribing a line.

❏ Add to each end of the arcs to make the arcs to the proper length:

  - ❏ Each arc is 3 times the diameter. The top diameter of the taper is 7" (Fig. 1). Therefore, the arc from C' to D' is 21". But the circumference of a 7" diameter circle is 22", which means the arc is 1" short (22" − 21" =1"). Add half of this (½") to each end of the top arc (Fig. 3) to make it the circumference

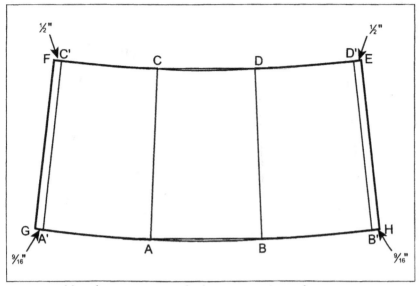

*Fig. 3: Add to the arcs to provide the correct circumference*

of a 7" diameter circle. This establishes points E and F.

❑ The bottom diameter of the taper is 8". Therefore the arc from A' to B' is 24". The circumference of an 8" circle is 25⅛", which means the arc is 1⅛" short. Add half of this (⁹⁄₁₆") to each end of the arc to make it the circumference of an 8" diameter circle. This establishes points G and H (Fig. 3).

❑ Draw end lines FG and EH.

Add allowances for seams and connections to complete the pattern.

## SWEEPING A TAPER

The layout for a centered taper can be developed by **sweeping a taper**. Sweeping a taper can only be done if the taper is centered and if the taper is fairly steep. This method cannot be used for a very gradual taper.

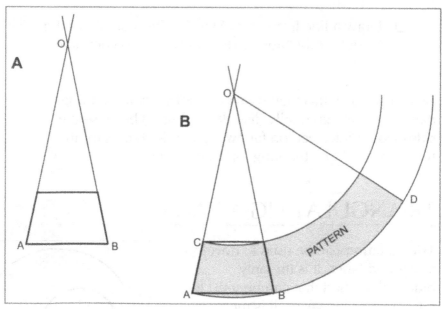

*Fig. 4: Sweeping a taper*

To sweep a taper (Fig. 4):

- ❏ Draw a full scale side view of the taper (Fig. 4A). Extend the side lines until they intersect at point O.

- ❏ With O as a center point, swing arcs an indefinite length from points A and C (Fig. 4B).

- ❏ Determine the circumference of the bottom circle of the taper and measure it around the bottom arc to locate point D (Fig. 4B). This can be done in either of two ways:

    - ❏ Line AB is the diameter of the bottom circle. Calculate the circumference of a circle of this diameter (Circumference = π x Diameter), and measure it around the arc to locate point D. (If you don't have a key for on your calculator, use 3.14 for .)

    - ❏ Set dividers to **half** of line AB (the radius of the circle). Step it off 6 times around the arc to locate point D.

❏ Draw a line from point D to O. This completes the layout for the taper. Add allowances to complete the pattern.

As you can see, this method would not work for a fitting that tapers very gradually (like that in Fig. 1) because the sides would intersect too far away, and the radius for the two arcs would be too long for practical use.

# TRIANGULATING A TAPER

**Triangulation** can be used to develop any round taper. It is the only practical method that can be used for offset tapers. However, it is more time-consuming than the other two methods of laying out a taper.

Triangulating a round taper uses the same method as a square-to-round:

❏ Draw a plan view.

❏ Draw in the layout lines.

❏ Find the true lengths.

❏ Triangulate from two known points to locate a third point.

Figure 5 is a plan view and elevation view of an offset round taper. To develop the layout, follow the steps listed above:

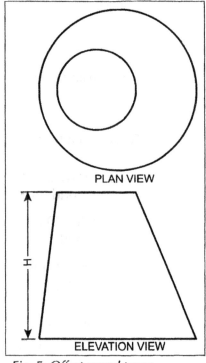

PLAN VIEW

ELEVATION VIEW

Fig. 5: Offset round taper

❏ Draw a half plan view (Fig. 6A). Divide each half circle into 6 equal spaces. Identify the points as shown—numbers on the small circle and letters on the large circle.

❏ Draw the layout lines as shown (Fig. 6A).

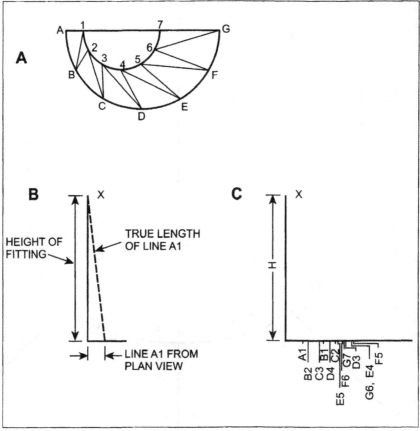

*Fig. 6: Start of layout for offset taper in Fig. 5*

❑ Find the true length of each layout line.

The true length triangle for line A1 is shown for illustration (Fig. 6B). In practice, one true length triangle (Fig. 6C) is used to find all lengths. The length of each line on the plan view (A1, B2, C3, etc.) is transferred to the base of the one true length triangle (Fig. 6C). The true length lines to be found are not drawn in because dividers are used to transfer the distances (X to point A1, X to point B2, etc.).

❑ Develop the pattern by triangulation. Start with a vertical line that is the true length of line A1 (Fig. 7A). To locate point B, triangulate from points A and 1. AB is a true length on the plan view because it lies on a horizontal plane. The distance B1 on the pattern is taken from the true length of B1 from Fig. 6C. Locate point B on both sides of line A1. Round tapers are generally made in a full pattern

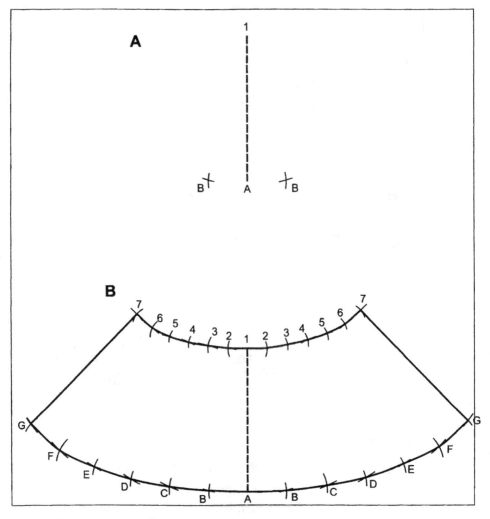

*Fig. 7: Pattern for the offset taper in Fig. 5*

rather than two half-patterns. By developing the points on each side of line A1, you will end up with a full pattern.

- ❏ To locate point 2, triangulate from B and 1 on both sides of line A1 (Fig. 7B). Distance 1-2 is a true length on the plan view.

- ❏ To locate point C, triangulate from points 2 and B on both sides of A1 (Fig. 7B).

- ❏ Locate the rest of the layout lines in the same way on both sides.

❏ Add allowances for seams and connections to complete the pattern.

# ROUND TEES

## PARALLEL LINES

**Round tees** (Fig. 1) are developed by a layout method called **parallel lines**. This chapter shows the basic principles of the parallel line method and some common shortcuts. Chapter 10 shows how the parallel line method is used to lay out round elbows.

The basic principle of layout—by triangulation or by parallel lines—is to find the actual lengths of lines so that they can be transferred to the pattern in the proper location and length.

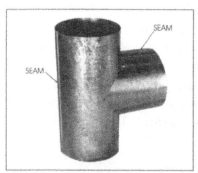

Fig. 1: The seam for the tee is located on the top of the tee. The seam for the duct is located opposite the tee

A **profile** is a cross section view of an object at a designated point. Parallel line layout uses profiles to locate equally spaced lines on the tee so that you can locate the same equal spaces on the layout.

The seam for a tee is located on the top of the tee (Fig. 1). The seam for the main duct is on the side of the duct opposite the tee (Fig. 1).

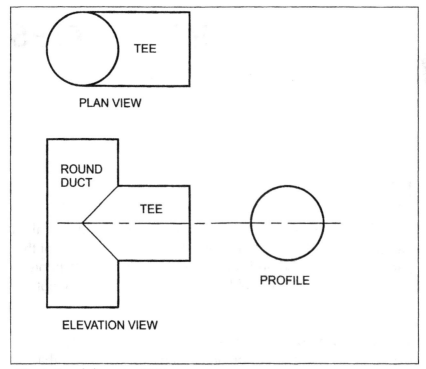

*Fig. 2: Equal diameter 90° tee*

## EQUAL DIAMETERS 90° TEE

Figure 2 shows the plan and elevation of an **equal diameters 90° tee**. This means that the tee intersects the round duct at 90° and that both ducts are the same diameter. A profile of the tee is drawn at the end of the tee in the elevation in Fig. 2. A profile allows you to locate equal spaces around a tee or round duct. The equal spaces are transferred to the stretchout.

Figure 3 shows how to lay out the equal diameter 90° tee in Fig. 2:

❑ Draw the full size elevation view of the tee (Fig. 3A).

❑ Establish the miter line of the tee. On a 90° equal diameters tee, the miter lines are simply 45° lines from the midpoint of the round duct (Fig. 3A).

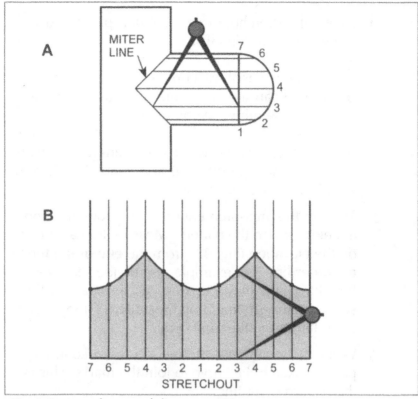

*Fig. 3: Layout of an equal diameters 90° tee*

❑ Add half the profile of the tee at the end of the tee. Divide the profile into 6 equal spaces and number it as shown. (Only half the profile is needed because the other half—for the other side of the tee—is exactly the same.)

❑ Draw parallel lines from each numbered point on the profile to the miter line as shown. Each of the lines on the tee is the actual length of the tee at that point.

This part of the procedure gives you the information needed to lay out the tee as shown in Fig. 3B:

❑ To start the pattern, draw the stretchout of the tee (line 7-7).
(The stretchout is the same as the circumference and can be calculated: Circumference = π x Diameter.)

- Divide the stretchout into 12 equal spaces and square up lines (Fig. 3B).
  (Each of these spaces is for one of the spaces around the tee as shown on the profile—6 for the spaces you can see on the elevation and 6 for the spaces on the other side of the tee.)

  Number the lines as shown. The seam for the tee is always on the top of the tee, so the numbering starts with 7, since this is the top of the tee.

- Transfer the measurement of each layout line from the elevation to the pattern. Measure the layout line on the elevation (Fig. 3A) from the **end of the tee** to the **miter line**. For example, use dividers to pick line 3 from the elevation (Fig. 3A) and transfer the same distance to line 3 on the pattern. Transfer the other lengths in the same way.

- When the length of each line is transferred to the pattern, sketch the curve to join the marks. This is the pattern miter line.

To complete the pattern, add allowances for seams and connections. Note the shape of the pattern. This is typical for any centered 90° tee.

# Shortcut—Use Quarter Profile

If you have done the layout just described, you have already realized that some of the layout lines are the same lengths:

- Lines 1 and 7 are the same.
- Lines 2 and 6 are the same.
- Lines 3 and 5 are the same.

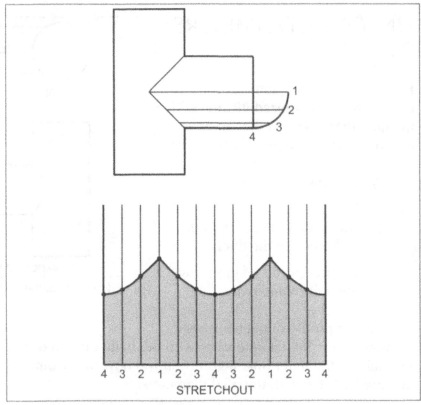

*Fig. 4: Shortcut method uses only a quarter profile*

In order to determine these lengths, only one quarter of the profile is needed, as shown in Fig. 4. These equally spaced points on the profile are labeled 1, 2, 3, and 4. The lines on the stretchout are numbered as shown in Fig. 4. Notice that the sequence of numbers repeats.

This method can only be used for a **centered tee**.

# THE HOLE FOR THE TEE

*Fig. 5: Hold the tee on the main duct to mark the hole*

The duct that the tee fits into must have a hole to match the tee miter lines. This can be laid out by parallel lines in the same way as the tee pattern. However, the hole is seldom developed. Instead, the formed tee is held against the pipe and the outline of the hole is traced around the miter lines (Fig. 5).

# UNEQUAL DIAMETERS 90° TEE

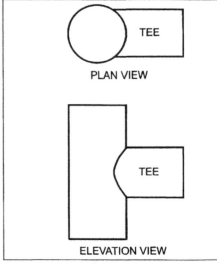

Figure 6 shows the plan and elevation for a **centered 90° tee with unequal diameters**. To lay out this tee, you need three profiles (Fig. 7A):

❑ Half profile of the tee at the end of the tee.

❑ Half profile of the main duct at the end of the duct.

❑ Quarter profile of the tee at the half profile of the duct.

*Fig. 6: Unequal diameters 90° tee*

The quarter profile of the tee is used to show where the tee intersects with the main duct in order to establish the miter line. Figure 7 shows how to lay out a centered 90° tee with unequal diameters:

❑ Draw the full-size elevation view of the tee (Fig. 7A).

❑ Add the half profile of the tee at the end of the tee. Divide the profile into 6 equal spaces and number it as shown (Fig. 7A). Draw parallel lines from the numbered points on the tee half profile.

❑ Add the half profile of the main duct at the end of the duct.

❑ Draw a **quarter** profile of the tee at the half profile of the duct (Fig. 7A). Number the quarter profile as shown. This numbering is important so that the lines on the elevation view and the corresponding lines on the quarter profile have the same number. Draw parallel lines from the tee quarter profile to the duct half profile (Fig. 7A).

❑ Where the quarter profile lines meet the half profile, draw parallel lines down.

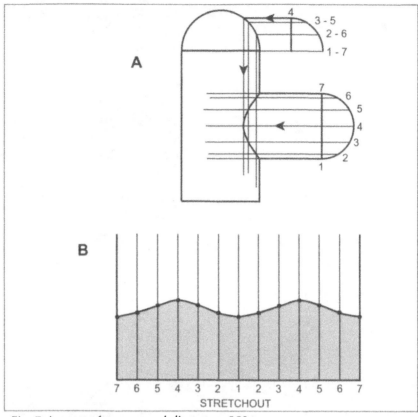

*Fig. 7: Layout of an unequal diameters 90° tee*

❑ Draw the miter line where the lines cross. For
   example, the miter line begins where line 7 from the
   tee intersects line 1-7 from the quarter profile. The
   next point is where line 6 from the tee intersects line
   2-6 from the quarter profile.

Once the miter line is established, the pattern for the tee is
developed (Fig. 7B) as it was for the equal diameters tee in
Fig. 3. Note the shape of the pattern. This is typical for any
unequal diameter, 90° tee.

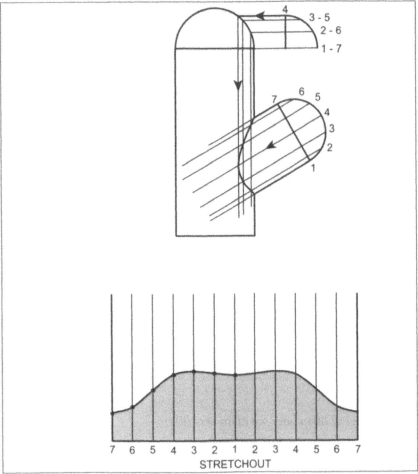

Fig. 8: Layout of a centered tee at a angle

# CENTERED TEE AT AN ANGLE

For a **centered tee at an angle** (Fig. 8), the miter line is an irregular curve. However, this tee can be laid out like the centered 90° tee with unequal diameters in Fig. 7. It requires the same three profiles:

- ❑ Half profile of the tee at the end of the tee.
- ❑ Half profile of the main duct at the end of the duct.
- ❑ Quarter profile of the tee at the half profile of the duct.

Figure 8 shows how to lay out a centered tee at an angle. Add allowances for seams and connections to complete the pattern.

# OFF-CENTER TEE

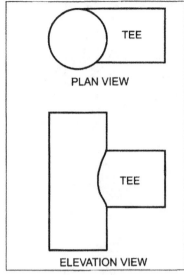

PLAN VIEW

TEE

ELEVATION VIEW

*Fig. 9: Off-center tee*

Figure 9 shows the plan and elevation for an **off-center tee**.

To lay out this tee, two views are needed:

- ❑ Plan view of the duct and tee with profile of the tee (Fig. 10A).

- ❑ Elevation view of the duct and tee with profile of the tee (Fig. 10B).

The full profiles are shown to make it easier to understand. (With experience, you can use only half profiles.) The plan view shows where the tee intersects with the main duct.

Figure 10 shows how to lay out an off-center tee:

- ❑ Draw the full-size **elevation view** of the tee (Fig. 10B).

  Add the full profile of the tee at the end of the tee as shown. Divide half the profile into 6 spaces (points 1 to 7). Draw parallel lines from the points. Number the points 8 to 12 on the other half of the profile as shown.

- ❑ Draw the **plan view** of the duct and tee (Fig. 10A). Make sure it is aligned with the elevation view.

  Draw a full profile of the tee on the plan view. Divide half the profile into 6 spaces. Draw parallel lines from the points to the surface of the plan view of the duct. Number the 12 points on the profile as shown (Fig. 10A). This is so the same lines on the plan and elevation have the same number.

  Number the points where the lines intersect on the

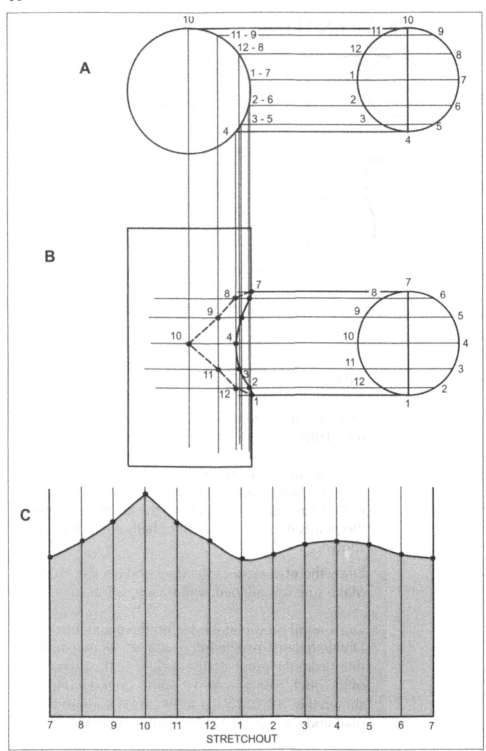

Fig. 10: Layout of an off-center tee

plan view as shown (Fig. 10A). Some of these points are identified with two different numbers from the tee profile (11-9, 12-8, etc.).

## Establishing the Miter Lines

From the points on the plan view of the duct (10, 11-9, 12-8, etc.) draw parallel lines down through the elevation view. The points where the parallel lines from the plan view intersect the lines on the elevation view mark the miter lines. Because the tee is off-center, the miter line on the back of the tee is different from the miter line on the front of the tee.

The **back miter line** is shown with a **dashed line** in Fig. 10B. It corresponds to points 7, 8, 9, 10, 11, 12, and 1 on the plan view. To mark the miter for the **back** of the fitting:

- ❑ Mark where line 10 from the plan view intersects line 10 from the tee profile (Fig. 10B).

- ❑ Mark where line 11 from the plan view intersects line 11 from the tee profile.

- ❑ Mark line 7, 8, 9, 12 and 1 in the same way.

The **front miter line** is shown with a **solid line** in Fig. 10B. It corresponds to points 1, 2, 3, 4, 5, 6, and 7 on the plan view. To mark the miter for the **front** of the fitting:

- ❑ Mark where lines 1, 2, 3, 4, 5, 6, and 7 from the plan view intersect the corresponding lines on the elevation view (Fig. 10B).

Number the points on the stretchout from 1 to 12 as shown in Fig. 10C. Transfer the lengths of the lines from the elevation to the layout. Be sure to keep track of the numbering system for the lines.

# ROUND ELBOWS

## LAYOUT OF A ROUND ELBOW

**Round elbows** (Fig. 1) are made in separate sections, called **gores**. Each of the gores has a round cross section. As with rectangular duct elbows, the **heel** (Fig. 1) is the outside curve of the elbow. The **throat** (Fig. 1) is the inside curve of the elbow. The **miter line** (Fig. 1) is the connecting line between gores.

A round elbow is commonly made of 4 pieces. However, it can be made of any number of pieces. The sheet metal worker who lays out the elbow generally determines how many pieces are to be used. If fewer pieces are used, the angles between gores will be greater. If more pieces are used, the radius will be closer to a smooth curve. More pieces are often used with a larger radius. A large, smooth radius is often needed for blowpipe work.

*Fig. 1: 4-piece 90° elbow*

## Draw the Side View

The first step in laying out the patterns for the gores is to draw a side view of the round elbow. The steps below are for a 4-piece, 8" diameter elbow with a 6" throat radius. To begin the layout for this elbow:

❑ **Swing the throat radius and the heel radius** (Fig. 2). From a square corner, swing a quarter circle with a

6" radius. Then measure over 8" and swing the heel radius.

❑ **Step off the proper number of the spaces on the throat arc** (Fig. 2). The number of spaces is **not** the number of pieces in the elbow. Use this equation:

Number of spaces = (2 × number of pieces) – 2

For a 4-piece elbow:

Number of spaces = (2 × 4 pieces) – 2
Number of spaces = 6

Step off 6 equal spaces on the heel (Fig. 2).

❑ **Draw the miter lines** (Fig. 3).
The end gore miter line is drawn through the mark for the first space. The middle gores are each two spaces (Fig. 3). This method of spacing makes all the angles of the gores the same so that the end gore pattern is the only pattern that you need to develop. You will see later how the middle gore pattern can be traced from it.

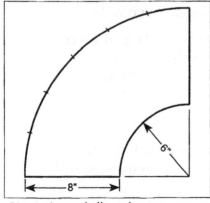

Fig. 2: Start of elbow layout

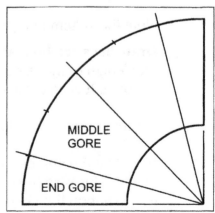

Fig. 3: Draw end gore and middle gores

- **Draw the elbow outline** (Fig. 4).
  Square lines up from points
  A and B to the first miter line.
  This outlines the end gore
  (Fig. 4).
  Only the end gore outline is
  needed, so the middle gore
  lines are seldom drawn.
  However, Fig. 4 shows that
  the lines for the middle gores
  are tangent to the arcs. This
  means that to establish line
  CD (Fig. 4), the distance OC
  and OD must be equal.

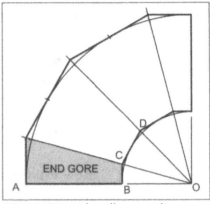

*Fig. 4: Draw the elbow outline*

# Develop the Pattern

Once the first gore of the elbow is drawn, the layout of the
gore pattern is by parallel lines (Fig. 5) and is practically the
same as for a round tee:

- **Draw the profile (Fig. 5A). Divide it into 6 equal
  spaces, number the points, and project lines up to
  the miter line.**

  Note the system of numbering on the profile.

- **Draw the stretchout and step off 12 equal spaces.**
  The length of the stretchout is the circumference of
  the duct. It is calculated with this equation:

  Circumference = Diameter x $\pi$.

  Note that the numbering on the stretchout starts
  with 4. This is so the seam will be on the side of the
  gore—not on the heel or throat. To avoid confusion,
  always use the same system to number the lines.

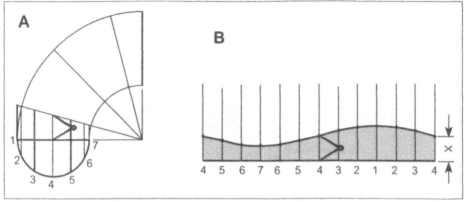

Fig. 5: Layout of first gore

☐ **Transfer distances from the end gore to the pattern** (Fig. 5B).
Set dividers to the length of line 4 on the gore (from the gore end line to the miter line). Transfer this distance to the pattern at the three points for line 4. Transfer all the lines from the end gore to the pattern in the same way. Sketch a curve through the points to complete the layout. Add allowances for seams and connections.

☐ **Trace the middle gore pattern using the end gore pattern** (Fig. 6).
The middle gore is simply two end gore patterns back-to-back. After the end gore is cut out, lay the pattern as shown in Fig. 6. Measure the distance 2X on each end of the metal. It will always be twice the distance of X (Fig. 5B) on the end gore pattern because the middle gore is two spaces and the end gore is one space. The dashed line indicates that the middle gore is two end gores, back-to-back.

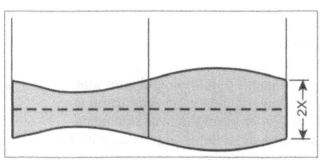

Fig. 6: Pattern for middle gore

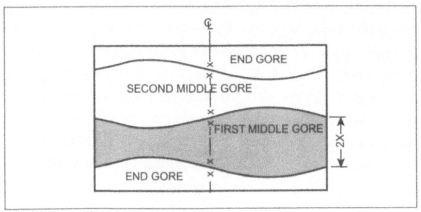

*Fig. 7: Second middle gore and end gore*

Add allowances for seams and connections. Cut out the middle gore. Trace a second middle gore from it. Trace a second end gore. This makes the four pieces for the elbow (Fig. 7).

# THINGS TO KNOW
# ABOUT ROUND ELBOWS

## Gore Seams

Seams for each gore are on the sides of the elbow—not on the heel or throat. This makes a more balanced appearance and also makes the elbow easier to fabricate.

## Staggered Seams

Seams are staggered. This means that if the end gore seam is on the near side of the elbow, the next gore seam is on the far side, and the third gore seam is on the near side again (Fig. 1). Staggered seams provide a better appearance and make the elbow easier to assemble.

Having staggered seams means that the end gore patterns must be rolled with the proper side IN. Middle gores cannot be rolled wrong.

For elbows with an **even number** of gores (2, 4, 6, etc.), the seams for the end gores are on opposite sides. For elbows with an **odd number** of gores (3, 5, 7, etc.), the seams for the end gores are on the same side.

## Prick Marking the Gores

Since the seams are staggered on opposite sides, the seams cannot be used to keep the gores aligned, so the elbow could become twisted when it is fabricated. To prevent this, **prick marks** (the X marks in Fig. 7) are made on the patterns. The prick marks are aligned with the seam of the previous gore to keep the elbow aligned.

## Growth

During fabrication an elbow often **grows** in the throat (Fig. 8). This means that the joint at the throat of the gores is not assembled as tight as it should be when the gores are being fabricated and assembled. On light metal, this is often because the metal edge does not go into the elbow edging machine as far as it should. On heavy metal, the thickness of the metal (unless a bevel is ground on it at the throat) holds the throat out slightly.

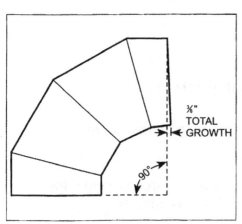

*Fig. 8: Growth on an elbow*

The result of **growth** is that the elbow throat becomes longer than it should be, and the elbow is actually less than

90° (Fig. 8). If the 4-piece elbow in Fig. 8 grows $\frac{1}{16}$" at **each edge** of each seam, each seam grows $\frac{1}{8}$" at the throat. Since there are three seams, the total growth throws the elbow $\frac{3}{8}$" off at the throat. It is no longer a 90° elbow.

On most light duct, elbow growth is ignored, because the lap seam connection with the next gore allows some "wiggling" to make up for the growth. However on heavy pipe where joints are butted and welded, growth can be an important consideration.

Growth is allowed for by altering the angle of the miter line on the layout slightly before the pattern is developed (Fig. 9). The amount of growth in an elbow depends upon many things such as the elbow throat radius, the thickness of the metal, and the skill of the fabricator. It is a matter of judgment based upon experience. In general, the smaller the throat radius, and the thicker the metal, the greater the growth.

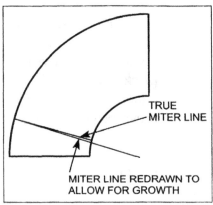

Fig. 9: Allowing for growth

# Calculating the Size of Pattern

The size of metal needed for the elbow patterns can be calculated:

❑ The length of the stretchout is the circumference for the elbow (Fig. 10). Calculate this with the equation:

Circumference = Diameter x π

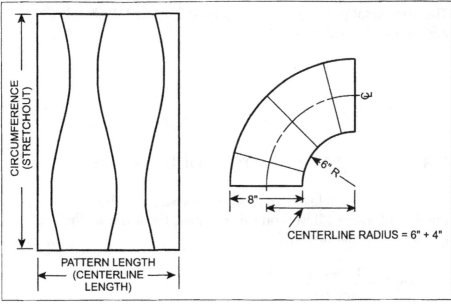

*Fig. 10: Metal size for pattern*

□ The other pattern length is the length of the elbow centerline (Fig. 10). This is ¼" of the circumference of a circle with the centerline radius:

□ Calculate the **centerline radius** as shown in Fig. 10: Centerline radius = Throat radius + Half the duct diameter

□ Calculate the **pattern length** (the **centerline length**):

$$\text{Pattern length} = \frac{\text{Centerline radius}}{2} \times \pi$$

**Example:**

What is the size of metal needed for a 4-piece, 8" diameter elbow with a throat radius of 6"?

Stretchout = Diameter × π
Stretchout = 8" × π
Stretchout = 25.13 (25 ⅛")

$$\text{Pattern length} = \frac{\text{Centerline radius}}{2} \times \pi$$

$$\text{Pattern length} = \frac{10}{2} \times \pi$$

Pattern length = 15.708 (15¹¹⁄₁₆")

The size metal needed for this elbow is 25⅛" x 15¹¹⁄₁₆" (plus allowances for seams and laps).

# Calculating the Degrees of the Gores

The number of angles in an elbow is the same as the number of spaces. Based on this number, the **angle of the gores** can be calculated:

$$\text{Angle} = \frac{\text{Degrees of elbow}}{\text{Number of spaces}}$$

For example, for a 4-piece, 90° elbow, the throat is divided into 6 equal spaces. This means that the gores form 6 equal angles (1 each for the end gores and 2 each for the middle gores). The angle can be calculated:

$$\text{Angle} = \frac{\text{Degrees of elbow}}{\text{Number of spaces}}$$

$$\text{Angle} = \frac{90°}{6}$$

$$\text{Angle} = 15°$$

This means that the first gore turns 15° and the middle gores turn 30°. Knowing the angle is handy because you can often use a 90° elbow pattern to make angles that you need. For example:

- ❑ The two end gores of a 4-piece elbow will form a 30° elbow (two 15° angles).

- ❑ Two end gores plus a middle gore will form a 60° elbow.

# LAYOUT BY RISE

An alternate method of layout for a round elbow is by using the **rise** of the elbow. The rise is the amount that the miter line rises above a horizontal line (Fig. 11). The rise can be determined in two ways:

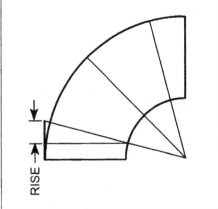

□  By drawing the first gore of the elbow and measuring the rise (Fig. 11)

□  By calculation, using a constant based on the number of pieces in the elbow:

Rise = Diameter × Constant

Fig. 11: Rise

For example, what is the rise for a 5-piece, 8" diameter, 90° elbow? According to the table in Fig. 12, the constant for a 5-piece elbow is 0.199. Use this in the equation:

Rise = Diameter × Constant
Rise = 8" × 0.199
Rise = 1.592 (1%₆")

| No of Pieces | Constant |
|:---:|:---:|
| 2 | 1.00 |
| 3 | 0.414 |
| 4 | 0.268 |
| 5 | 0.199 |
| 6 | 0.159 |
| 7 | 0.132 |
| 8 | 0.113 |
| 9 | 0.098 |
| 10 | 0.089 |
| 11 | 0.0787 |
| 12 | 0.0714 |

Fig. 12: Constants for calculating rise for 90° elbows

110

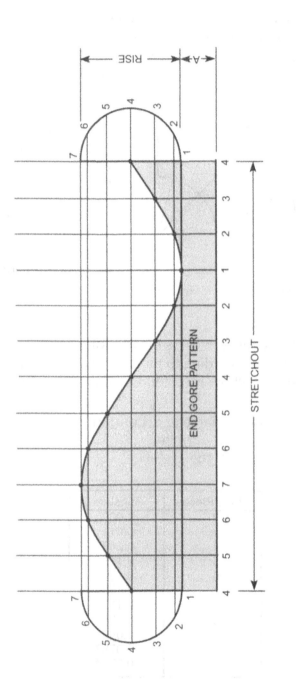

NOT TO SCALE

Fig. 13: Layout by rise

# Developing Layout by Rise

The layout by rise is shown in Fig. 13:

- [ ] Draw the stretchout to the proper length. Divide the stretchout into 12 equal spaces. Square up lines from these points and number the lines as shown (Fig. 13).

- [ ] Swing half-circles at each end of the stretchout, using half the amount of rise as the radius (Fig. 13).

- [ ] Divide both half-circles into 6 equal spaces and number the points as shown. Project lines from one half circle to the other.

- [ ] Mark the point where **rise line 4** intersects **stretchout line 4** (at three points). Mark where each rise line intersects each corresponding stretchout line in the same way. Connect these points to outline the curves of the pattern (Fig. 13).

- [ ] To determine the length of dimension A (Fig. 13), calculate the stretchout of the throat radius of the elbow, which will be ¼ the circumference of a circle of that radius. The easiest equation to use for the **throat radius stretchout** is:

$$\text{Stretchout} = \frac{\text{Throat radius}}{2} \times \pi$$

If the throat radius is 6", then the throat radius stretchout is:

$$\text{Stretchout} = \frac{6}{2} \times \pi$$

$$\text{Stretchout} = 9.425"$$

To determine dimension A (Fig. 13), divide the throat radius stretchout by the number of divisions in the elbow. For a 5-piece elbow, there are 8 divisions: (5 x 2) - 2 = 8. Calculate dimension A:

$$\text{Dimension A} = \frac{9.425"}{8}$$

Dimension A = 1.178 (1$\frac{3}{16}$")

If dimension A is a small amount, such as 1$\frac{13}{16}$", usually another inch is added to the end gores to make them easier to fabricate. (The extra inch is not added to the middle gores.)

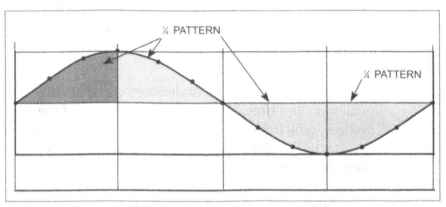

*Fig. 14: A quarter pattern of the curve can be used to form the full pattern*

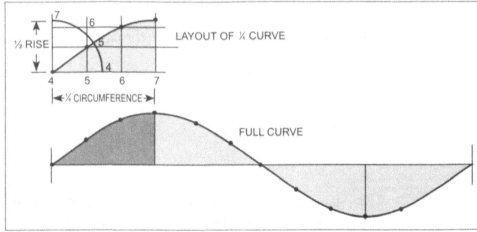

*Fig. 15: Shortcut layout by quarter pattern*

# Shortcut Layout by Quarter Pattern

A shortcut method of layout by rise is based upon the fact that the curve of one-fourth of the elbow gore pattern is repeated on the other quarters of the pattern (Fig. 14). You can see in Fig. 14 that the quarter pattern can be moved and flipped to form the full pattern.

Figure 15 shows the layout of the quarter pattern. Note that half the rise and a quarter of the stretchout is used. The numbering and spaces are the same as in the full layout in Fig. 13.

# *INDEX*